Practical Descriptive Geometry

Books by Hiram E. Grant

PRACTICAL DESCRIPTIVE GEOMETRY (McGRAW-HILL)
PRACTICAL DESCRIPTIVE GEOMETRY PROBLEMS (PUBLISHED BY THE AUTHOR)

Co-author with Prof. H. C. Spencer

TECHNICAL DRAWING PROBLEMS, SERIES 2 (MACMILLAN)
THE BLUEPRINT LANGUAGE (MACMILLAN)
TECHNICAL LETTERING PRACTICE (MACMILLAN)

Practical Descriptive Geometry

HIRAM E. GRANT, *Professor and Head*
Department of Engineering Drawing
Washington University, St. Louis

McGraw-Hill Book Company, Inc.
New York   Toronto   London
1952

PRACTICAL DESCRIPTIVE GEOMETRY

Library of Congress Catalog Card Number: 52-5333

V

THE MAPLE PRESS COMPANY, YORK, PA.

This descriptive geometry textbook attempts to correlate and integrate theory and practice instead of considering each a separate entity. The transition from theory to practice is not necessarily obvious. Practical problems, because of the nature of their given information, frequently cannot be solved without considerable difficulty if an attempt is made to derive their solutions by using the typical theoretical approach. This is due to the difference between the factors that control the design of the practical and theoretical problems. Components of the machine or job control the practical problem's given information, while author and teacher have complete control over the theoretical problem. For example, a theoretical problem would normally ask that a line be drawn tangent to a given parabola, while a practical problem would ask that a parabola be drawn tangent to a given line (see Fig. 196a).

The *direct method* is used because it is the only feasible method to use with practical problems. Since the origin of the direct method may be of interest to many, a brief history is included.

Assistant Dean Emeritus Adam V. Millar, of the University of Wisconsin, was the first to conceive the idea of the direct method in 1906 or 1907, after examining Fig. 21, dealing with a line piercing a plane, in A. E. Church's *Descriptive Geometry and Shades and Shadows*. The traces of the plane had been omitted from the illustration. Dean Millar reasoned that if this problem could be solved without the traces of the plane, others could also be solved in the same manner. He prepared a mimeographed set of notes based on this new method and used it for the first time in a University of Wisconsin summer session class in 1908. The first book using this new method was written by Millar and Maclin in 1913, but it did not include auxiliary views. They were added when the second edition written by Millar, Maclin, and Marquardt appeared in 1919. The book is now in its fourth edition and its authors are Millar and Shiels. However, Dean Millar did use several auxiliary views in an otherwise Mongean method book he wrote with Professor Phillips in 1909, entitled *Essentials of Descriptive Geometry*. Although Dean Millar originated the new method, he did not give it a name. Professor George J. Hood in his *Geometry of Engineering Drawing*, published in 1926, called it the direct method, which has become its now commonly accepted name.

The reference plane is used in this book because it orientates the student's spatial visualization much better than the reference or ground line does. Although the reference or ground line actually represents the edge view of the reference plane, it is not identified by the student as the edge view. It becomes a line without any spatial significance *to the student*, and for that reason measurements from it are made on a rule-of-thumb basis.

Since accuracy is a vital part of drafting, a chapter has been devoted to it. Frequent reference to the chapter and emphasis of the importance of accuracy should help to make the student conscious of its importance, should alert him to inaccuracies and aid him in keeping them to a minimum.

Problems are not included in this text, because a special set of problems entitled *Practical Descriptive Geometry Problems* has been designed for use with this book. The set of problems, which has been used in about fifty schools during the past four years, includes a number of problems to be completely laid out by the student. A text assignment key to this text accompanies each problem book. Teachers preferring to use other problem books with this text may secure the text assignment key for the problem book of their choice by writing the author of this text.

The author wishes to acknowledge the encouragement given him over a period of years by Professor H. D. Orth, under whom he taught for the first time. He also wishes to acknowledge the cooperation of Professor H. C. Spencer, with whom he has written two other books. Professor E. J. Nystrom, Helsinki, Finland; Professor Dr. Erwin Kruppa, Vienna, Austria; Professor F. P. Bustraan, Hilversum, Holland; Professor Angel Taibo, Buenos Aires, Argentina; and Professor A. Dickason, Birmingham, England have given valuable assistance as well as permission to use illustrations from their books; and to them the author expresses his deepest gratitude.

The teachers who will use this book may in a very constructive way influence its future editions by sending their criticisms and suggestions to the author.

HIRAM E. GRANT

St. Louis, Missouri
May, 1952

CONTENTS

Preface v

Chapter 1 INTRODUCTION 1

Chapter 2 REFERENCE PLANES 3

Chapter 3 THE BASIC LINES AND PLANES 12

Chapter 4 BASIC AUXILIARY VIEWS 17

Chapter 5 POINTS AND LINES 31

Chapter 6 LINES AND PLANES 43

Chapter 7 REVOLUTION 84

Chapter 8 FORCE DIAGRAMS 108

Chapter 9 POINT, LINE, AND PLANE RELATIONS WITH CYLINDERS,
CONES, AND SPHERES 113

Chapter 10 CONIC SECTIONS AND THEIR APPLICATIONS 125

Chapter 11 MINING, GEOLOGY, AND CIVIL ENGINEERING . . . 135

Chapter 12 SHADES AND SHADOWS 144

Chapter 13 CURVED SURFACES 154

Chapter 14 PLANE AND CURVED SURFACE INTERSECTIONS . . . 175

Chapter 15 DEVELOPMENTS, TRANSITIONS, AND THE HELIX . . . 183

Chapter 16 INTERSECTION OF SURFACES 205

Chapter 17 GRAPHICAL ACCURACY 243

Index 249

CHAPTER 1

INTRODUCTION

1. DESCRIPTIVE GEOMETRY

Descriptive geometry as we know it today (without regard to method of presentation) was originated by Gaspard Monge of France in the eighteenth century. His method of presentation is known as the Mongean method. A brief history of the origin of the direct method which is used in this book is found in the preface. A majority of the recent American textbooks used in colleges and universities use the direct method of presentation.

This subject is taught by one method or the other (and in a few colleges by a combination of the two methods) in almost every engineering school throughout the world for the express purpose of teaching the student to visualize through the development of his ability to analyze and reason. It is therefore very necessary that the student *understand* the cardinal principles of this subject in order to analyze and reason the problems to their correct solutions.

2. HOW TO STUDY

Some students experience a slow start in this subject primarily because of their inability to analyze and reason as well as their inability to visualize. To attempt to see how someone else solves the problems merely adds to the difficulty. The mechanics of most of the solutions are usually quite easy to follow. What is missed completely in seeing another student's solution is the opportunity for improvement in the ability to analyze, reason, and visualize that the problem offers. Only a thorough study of the assignments—this means studying the assignment *several* times—and *absolutely no reference to the text* while the problems are being solved will, in due time, produce the desired results.

A physical education instructor cannot build up a student's muscles, but he can guide him if the student does the necessary work. This analogy applies to descriptive geometry as well as to most other subjects. The text and the professor in charge of the class can help if the student does an adequate job of studying and asks to have hazy points clarified. But, again, if the student is to improve materially, he must study until each fundamental is clear.

Although it is tempting to leave a text open and attempt, with perhaps occasional success, to solve a problem by keeping one eye on the text and the other on the problem, the problem should be solved without using the text. Using the text as a direct aid in solving the problems is, for all practical purposes, copying. A much more satisfactory procedure is to study the assignments well, then close the text and go to work on the problems. It will not be long before the student develops confidence in himself.

Some students have the mistaken notion that, if they see the solution, they will understand it. If "seeing" a solution is learning, then giving the student the solutions to 2,000 or even 5,000 problems would be the answer to learning. Unfortunately, knowledge cannot be so easily acquired. A student who has examined 5,000 solutions would most likely fail any examination in which he were required to analyze, reason, and visualize in order to solve the problems.

3. QUALITY OF DRAFTSMANSHIP

Good quality of draftsmanship should come from the student voluntarily and not as a requirement of the professor in order to pass the course. Pride in one's work should be the chief motivating force. The better students invariably take pride in their work and *want* to produce neat-looking drawings. Pride in their work, good study habits, good methods of procedure in solving their problems, and a willingness to work have gone a long way toward placing them among the better students.

CHAPTER 2

REFERENCE PLANES

4. REGULAR REFERENCE PLANES

Each and every view in engineering drawing is drawn on a reference plane, although it may not be thought of as such. The front view is drawn on the frontal reference plane (abbreviated FRP), the top view on the horizontal reference plane (HRP), and the side view on the profile reference plane (PRP). These three planes are mutually perpendicular to each other. When one of the three planes is true size, the other two reference planes appear in their edge views.

5. FRONTAL REFERENCE PLANE

The frontal reference plane (FRP) is true size in the front view and appears as a horizontal line in the top view and as a vertical line in the side view. The FRP as shown in Fig. 1 may be placed in its edge view in one of several positions in the top view. Generally, the most convenient position is used; whether it be placed at the front, in the middle, or to the rear is dependent upon the problem to be solved. Note that all FRP positions are perpendicular to the horizontal reference plane.

In order that a reference plane appear true size in a given view, it *must* appear as a line (its edge view) in an adjacent view and perpendicular to the line of sight (projection lines) between the two views. Thus, FRP must appear as a horizontal line in the top view and as a vertical line in the side view, otherwise FRP would not be true size in the front view.

6. HORIZONTAL REFERENCE PLANE

The horizontal reference plane (HRP) is true size in the top view and appears as a horizontal line (edge view) in both the front and side views. The HRP as shown in Fig. 2 may be at any elevation (height) in the front view from the highest to the lowest position. Note that every position of the HRP is perpendicular to the FRP.

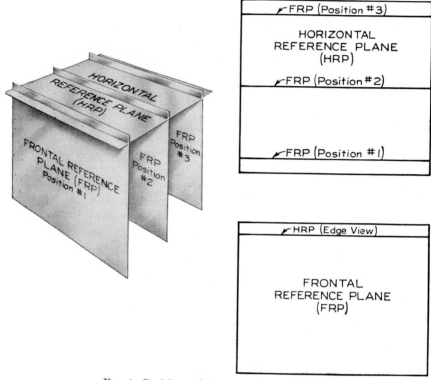

Fig. 1. Positions of frontal reference planes.

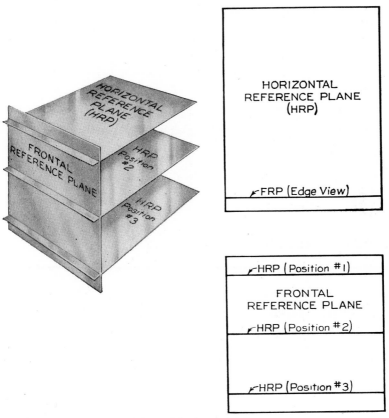

FIG. 2. Positions of horizontal reference planes.

7. PROFILE REFERENCE PLANE

The profile reference plane (*PRP*) of Fig. 3 is true size in the side view and appears as a vertical line (edge view) in both top and front views. The *PRP* may appear as a vertical line in the right portion, in the middle or left portion of both top and front views.

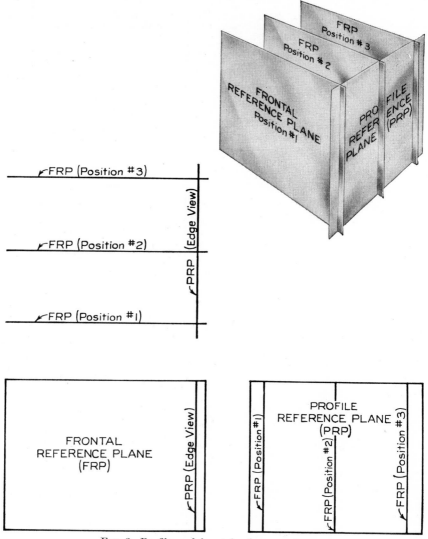

Fig. 3. Profile and frontal reference planes.

8. REFERENCE PLANES GENERALIZATION

Whenever two planes are perpendicular to each other and one appears true size in a given view, the other plane *must* appear as an edge in that view. This is illustrated in Fig. 4, where *HRP* appears in its edge view when *FRP* appears true size. In Fig. 5, *PRP* appears true size in the side view while *FRP* appears in a vertical position in its edge view.

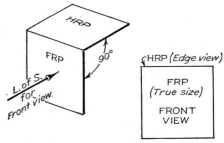

Fig. 4. Relationship of *FRP* with *HRP*.

9. AN ENGINEERING DRAWING

Most engineering drawings represent machine parts, structural members, etc.; thus they have body and weight. Figure 6 is typical of them. Assume the front and top views as the given views and the right side view as the view required to be drawn. Each corner of the front view is projected horizontally to the right side view.

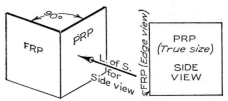

Fig. 5. Relationship of *FRP* with *PRP*.

The next step is to obtain the dimensions which must be measured *along* the horizontal projection lines from the front view for the purpose of locating the various points in the side view. These dimensions will be obtained in a vertical direction *only on the paper* in the top view. The top view of the front face of the object is commonly used as a base line from which measurements may be made. Of the nine corners of the numbered surface, corner 1 is on the front face as shown in the top view. Corner 1 will also be on the side view of the front face of the object and may be located in the side view by projecting corner 1 from the front view horizontally to the right side view until the projection line intersects a vertical line in the side view which will represent the side view of the front face of the object.

It is advisable to number corner 1 in the side view as has been done in Fig. 6. Corner 2 in the top view is dimension d_2 from the front face of the object. To locate corner 2 in the side view, project the front view of corner 2 from the front view and measure d_2 from the side view of the front face *along* the horizontal projection line of corner 2 and number the corner. Corner 3 in the top view is dimension d_1 from the top view of the front face. Project the front view of corner 3 horizontally to the side view, then measure d_1 from the side view of the front face along this projection line and number the located corner. This corner is lower than either corner 1 or 2 and is not so far from the front of the object as is corner 2. In a similar manner, locate the remainder of the nine corners

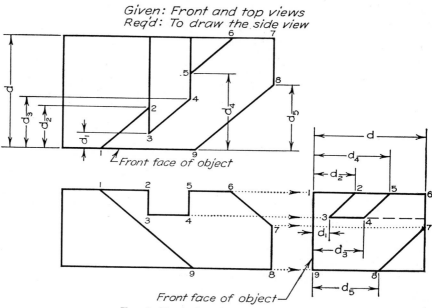

Given: Front and top views
Req'd: To draw the side view

FIG. 6. Typical engineering drawing.

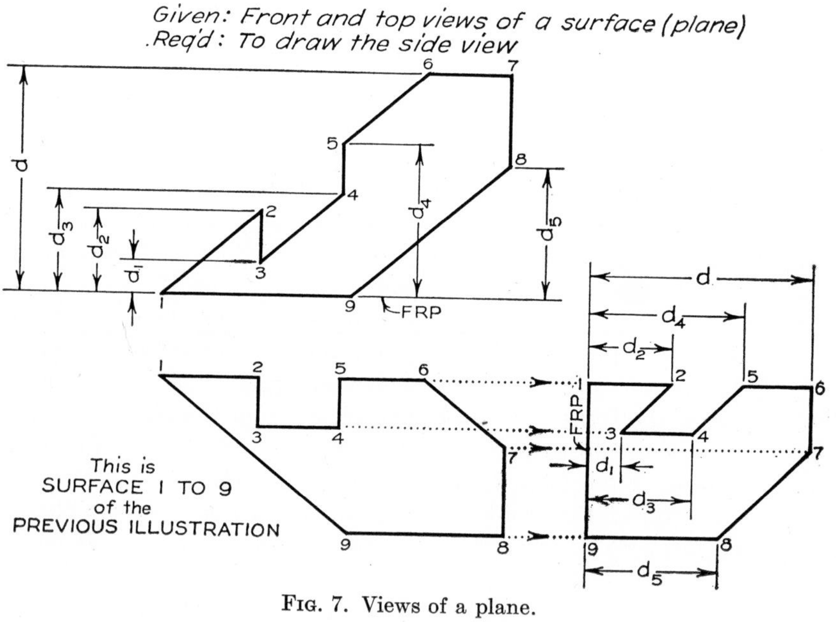

Given: Front and top views of a surface (plane)
Req'd: To draw the side view

This is
SURFACE 1 TO 9
of the
PREVIOUS ILLUSTRATION

FIG. 7. Views of a plane.

and then connect them in the same consecutive manner as they are connected in the top view. The other surfaces will be similarly located in the side view.

10. VIEWS OF A PLANE

In descriptive geometry many of the problems will not involve objects as represented in Fig. 6. Instead, the problems will involve *only* planes and lines. In Fig. 7 *only* one plane of Fig. 6 is represented in the given front and top views. It has *no* thickness.

Since this surface is not an object and there is no front face, the frontal reference plane (*FRP*) is used as a base line for dimensions d to d_5. The front face of the object in Fig. 6 and *FRP* in Fig. 7 are actually the *same* plane but only spoken of in different terms. The corners of the plane are located in the side view in the *same* way and with the same dimensions as they were when they were on the object in Fig. 6.

In Fig. 8 the plane *ABC* (not an object) has been projected onto the

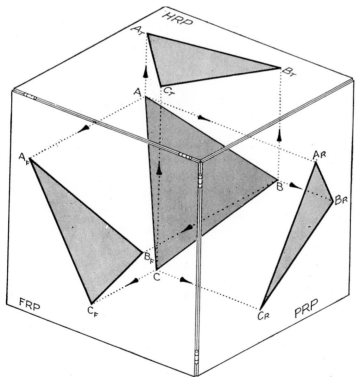

FIG. 8. Projection of a plane onto the reference planes.

three reference planes to create the top, front, and right side views of the plane. Figure 9 shows the orthographic views of the plane ABC.

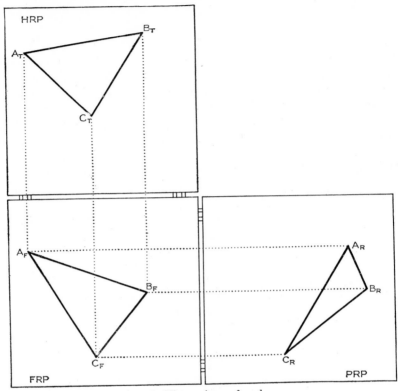

FIG. 9. Three views of a plane.

11. CONSTRUCTION OF A VIEW

In constructing a new view, locate the reference plane to be used as a base line for the dimensions in a given view as well as in the new view as shown in step 2 of Fig. 10. Since A is on FRP, no dimension is necessary. Project A_F to the top view, and put it on FRP in that view as shown in step 3. Point B_F is projected to the top view from the front view and located *along* that projection line using dimension d obtained from the side view. Point C is similarly located by measuring dimension d_1 from FRP as shown in step 4.

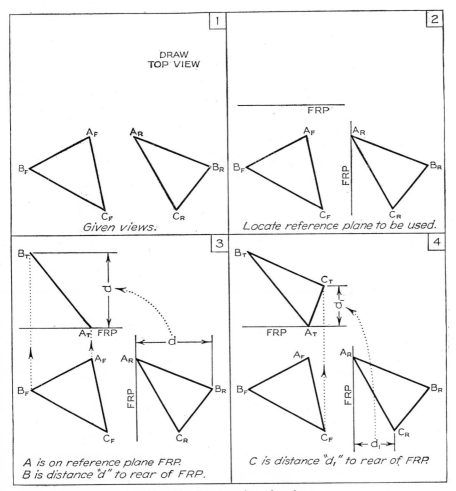

FIG. 10. Construction of a view.

CHAPTER 3

THE BASIC LINES AND PLANES

12. NORMAL LINES (or Edges of Objects)

A **normal line** (or edge) is parallel to two of the three regular reference planes. It will appear true length in two of the views and as a point in the third view (see Fig. 11).

T.L. = TRUE LENGTH

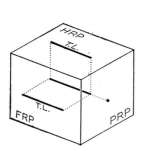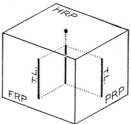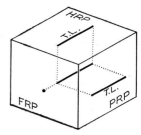

Fig. 11. Normal lines.

13. INCLINED LINES (or Edges of Objects)

An **inclined line** (or edge) is parallel to only one reference plane. It is at an acute angle to the other two reference planes. The line is true length in one view and foreshortened in the other two views (see Fig. 12).

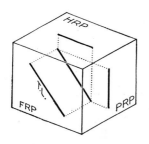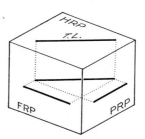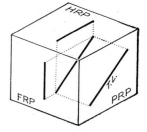

Fig. 12. Inclined lines.

14. OBLIQUE LINES (or Edges of Objects)

An **oblique line** (or edge) is not parallel to any of the three regular reference planes. Thus, this line is foreshortened in all three regular views (see Fig. 13).

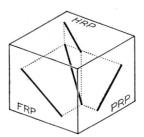

Fig. 13. Oblique lines.

15. NORMAL PLANES (or Surfaces)

A **normal plane** (or surface) is perpendicular to two of the regular reference planes and parallel to the third. It will appear true size in one view and as an edge view in the other two regular views (see Fig. 14).

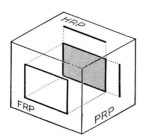 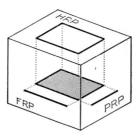 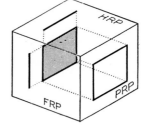

Fig. 14. Normal planes.

16. INCLINED PLANES (or Surfaces)

An **inclined plane** (or surface) is perpendicular to one reference plane and at acute angles to the other two reference planes. In its edge view, this plane will appear in an inclined position in one view and as a foreshortened plane in the other two regular views (see Fig. 15).

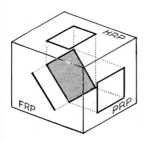 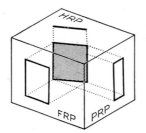 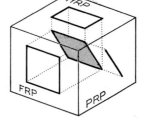

Fig. 15. Inclined planes.

17. OBLIQUE PLANES (or Surfaces)

An **oblique plane** is not perpendicular to any of the three regular reference planes and appears as a foreshortened plane in each of the three regular views (see Fig. 16).

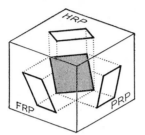

FIG. 16. Oblique planes.

18. HORIZONTAL LINES (or Edges of Objects)

Any line (or edge) lying in or parallel to *HRP* is a **horizontal line**. Thus, certain normal and inclined lines may also come under the heading of horizontal lines (see Fig. 17). All horizontal lines of the object are not represented by solid ink lines.

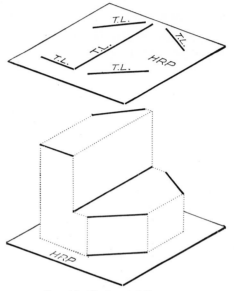

FIG. 17. Horizontal lines.

19. FRONTAL LINES (or Edges of Objects)

Any line (or edge) lying in or parallel to *FRP* is a **frontal line**. Frontal lines may also be classified as normal or inclined lines (see Fig. 18). All frontal lines of the object are not represented by solid ink lines.

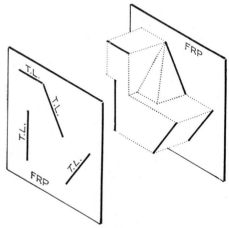

FIG. 18. Frontal lines.

20. PROFILE LINES (or Edges of Objects)

Any line (or edge) lying in or parallel to *PRP* is a **profile line.** These lines likewise may be classified as normal or inclined lines (see Fig. 19). All profile lines of the object are not represented by solid ink lines.

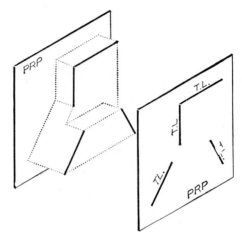

Fig. 19. Profile lines.

21. A THEORETICAL LINE

A **theoretical line,** although represented by a definite length of line such as *AB* of Fig. 20, is *infinite* in length. Do *not* consider lines to be limited by their given lengths in theoretical problems. Instead, feel free to extend them. In practical problems, it is also sometimes feasible to extend the lines (or edges of objects) in order to facilitate solving the problem.

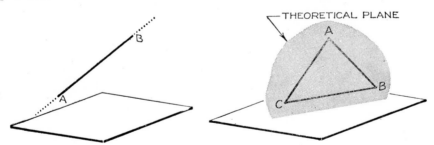

Fig. 20. A theoretical line.   Fig. 21. A theoretical plane.

22. A THEORETICAL PLANE

A **theoretical plane** (Fig. 21), although represented by definite lines and points, is *infinite* in extent. Do not consider planes to be limited by their given lines in theoretical problems. The lines representing the plane may be extended, or new lines may be added to the plane. In practical problems, it may be necessary to extend a plane beyond the portion required by the result in order to solve the problem more readily.

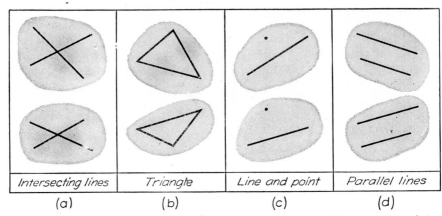

| Intersecting lines | Triangle | Line and point | Parallel lines |
| (a) | (b) | (c) | (d) |

The plane may be represented in space by the above lines and points. However, it should be realized that they do <u>not</u> define the limits of the planes.

Fig. 22. Representing a plane.

23. REPRESENTING A PLANE

A plane may be represented by lines or points or a combination of the two. Figure 22 shows four ways in which a plane may be represented. These lines and points merely establish the position of the plane in space but do *not* control its size.

CHAPTER 4

BASIC AUXILIARY VIEWS

24. WHAT IS AN AUXILIARY VIEW?

An **auxiliary view** is any view taken in such a manner that the line of sight of the view is not parallel with the line of sight of the front, top, or side views. For example, assume that the true size of an inclined plane is desired. The line of sight necessary to determine the true size of this plane must be perpendicular to the edge view of the inclined plane. The line of sight that is perpendicular to the inclined plane is at an acute angle to two of the regular reference planes and parallel to the third.

25. AUXILIARY REFERENCE PLANE

Assume that the line of sight shown in Fig. 23 is perpendicular to an inclined plane. The view taken in that direction would be an auxiliary view. The plane on which that view would be drawn would be called an **auxiliary reference plane** (*ARP*).

26. AUXILIARY VIEWS PROJECTED OFF THE TOP VIEW

Any auxiliary view projected off the top view will be drawn on an auxiliary reference plane (*ARP*), Fig. 23, which is perpendicular to *HRP*. When *ARP* is true size in the auxiliary view, *HRP* will appear in its edge view (as a line) and perpendicular to the line of sight (projection lines) between the auxiliary and top views. The *ARP* will in turn appear in its edge view in the top view where *HRP* is true size. Figure 24 shows the foreshortening of *FRP* and *PRP* in the auxiliary view projected off the top view.

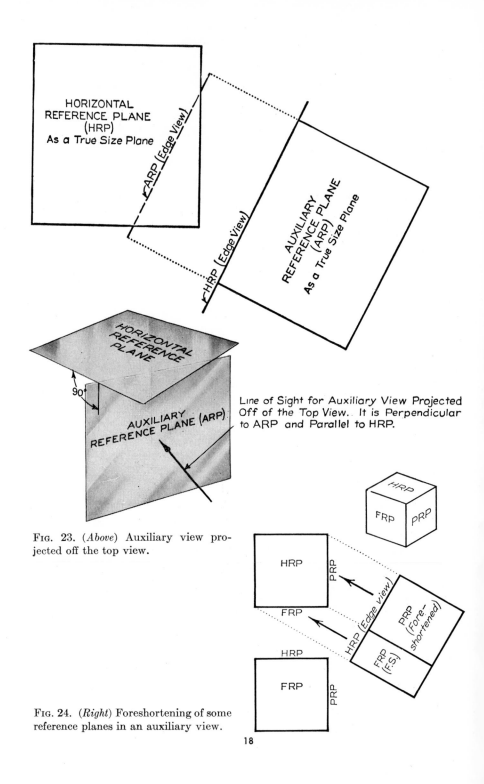

HORIZONTAL
REFERENCE PLANE
(HRP)
As a True Size Plane

ARP (Edge View)

HRP (Edge View)

AUXILIARY
REFERENCE PLANE
(ARP)
As a True Size Plane

HORIZONTAL
REFERENCE
PLANE

90°

AUXILIARY
REFERENCE PLANE (ARP)

Line of Sight for Auxiliary View Projected
Off of the Top View. It is Perpendicular
to ARP and Parallel to HRP.

FIG. 23. (*Above*) Auxiliary view projected off the top view.

HRP

FRP   PRP

HRP

PRP

FRP

HRP (Edge view)

PRP
(Fore-shortened)

HRP

FRP

PRP

FRP
(F.S.)

FIG. 24. (*Right*) Foreshortening of some reference planes in an auxiliary view.

Figure 25 shows three views of the plane ABC. The points A, B, and C are projected to the auxiliary view, thereby establishing the width of the auxiliary view. The measurements to be measured *along* the projection lines with HRP as a base line are obtained from the front view, where the HRP is again shown in its edge view. Point A_F is distance d below HRP and is transferred to the auxiliary view to locate A_A. Similar measurements are made for points B_A and C_A. Note measurement d in the pictorial. *All* measurements to be measured along the projection lines in *any* auxiliary view projected off the top view must be obtained from some other view where HRP appears in its edge view.

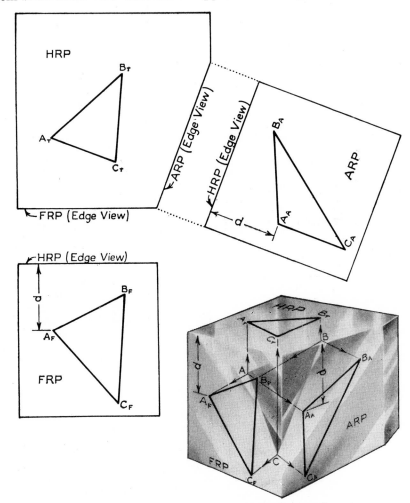

FIG. 25. Auxiliary view projected off the top view.

27. AUXILIARY VIEWS PROJECTED OFF THE FRONT VIEW

Any auxiliary view projected off the front view will be drawn on an auxiliary reference plane (*ARP*), Fig. 26, which is perpendicular to *FRP*. In the auxiliary view *FRP* will appear in its edge view, while in the front

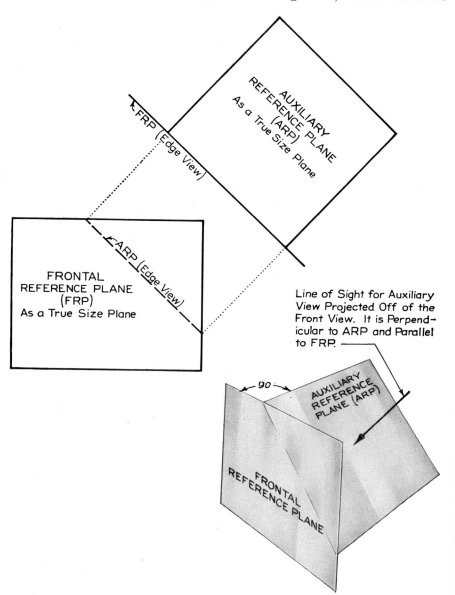

FIG. 26. Auxiliary view projected off the front view.

view *ARP* will appear in its edge view. The *FRP* in the auxiliary view will be perpendicular to the line of sight (projection lines) between the two views.

Figure 27 shows that the measurements in the auxiliary view measured *along* the projection lines must be measured from *FRP* and that they may be obtained in the top view where *FRP* again appears in its edge view. Measurement d obtained from the top view locates point A_A in the auxiliary view. Similar measurements will locate points B_A and C_A.

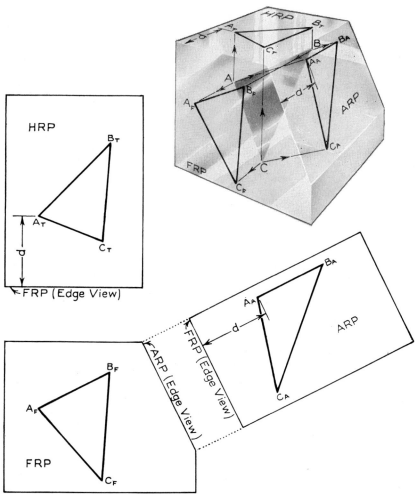

FIG. 27. Auxiliary view projected off the front view.

28. AUXILIARY VIEWS PROJECTED OFF THE SIDE VIEW

Any auxiliary view projected off the side view will be drawn on an auxiliary reference plane (*ARP*), Fig. 28, which is perpendicular to *PRP*. In the auxiliary view *PRP* will appear in its edge view, while in the side view *ARP* will appear in its edge view. The *PRP* in the auxiliary view will be perpendicular to the line of sight (projection lines) between the two views.

Figure 29 shows that the measurements in the auxiliary view measured *along* the projection lines must be measured from *PRP* and that they may be obtained from the front view where *PRP* again appears in its edge view.

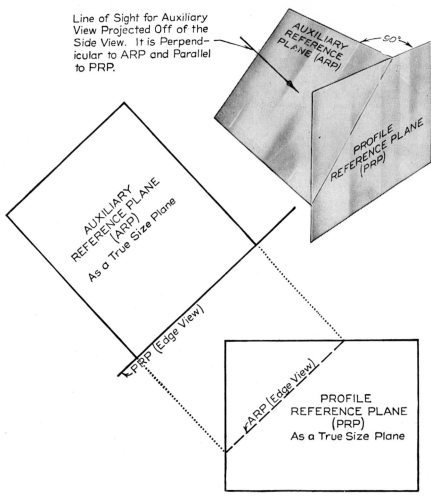

FIG. 28. Auxiliary view projected off the side view.

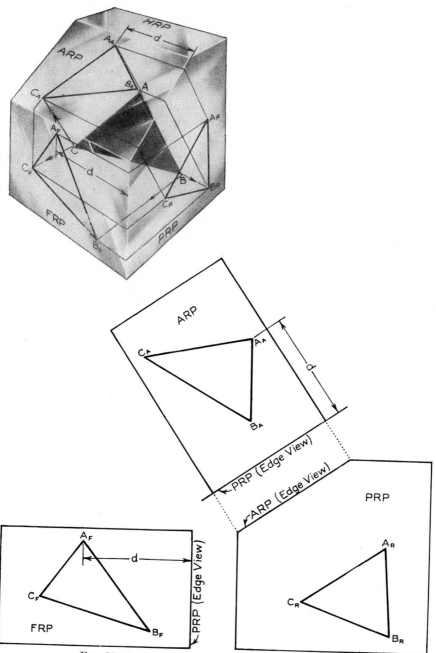

FIG. 29. Auxiliary view projected off the side view.

Measurement d obtained from the front view locates point A_A in the auxiliary view. Similar measurements are made to locate points B_A and C_A in the auxiliary view.

29. POINTS COMMON TO ALL AUXILIARY VIEWS

There are two things in common to *all* views, auxiliary and regular views, projected from *one* view which may therefore be called the **common view.** Note that in Fig. 30 the five views are all projected from the same view which has been labeled as the *common view.* The first item common to all views: the pencil point is farthest from the common view in all views projected from it. The pencil point will *never* be closest to the common view in one view and farthest from it in the next. The second item common to all views: measurements d and d_1 as they are measured *along* the projection lines are the same in *all* views projected off the common view. Thus, if the common view and only one of the auxiliary views were given, all the other views could be drawn.

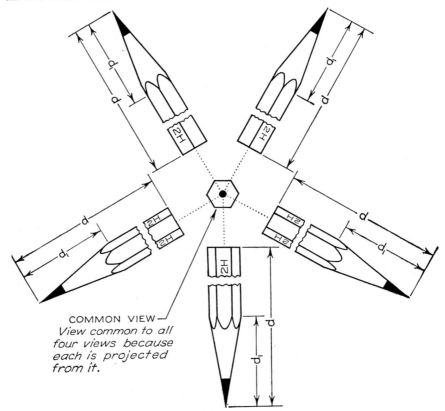

COMMON VIEW
*View common to all
four views because
each is projected
from it.*

FIG. 30. The common view.

30. DIRECTION OF EDGE VIEW OF REFERENCE PLANE IN AN AUXILIARY VIEW

· *Assume* that Fig. 31 deals with a series of auxiliary views projected off the top view. The reference plane appearing in its edge view in each of these auxiliary views would be *HRP*. The rectangle representing the true size view of this reference plane would be *HRP* upon which the top view is drawn. Since *HRP* is true size in the top view, the edge view of *HRP* must be perpendicular to the line of sight between the top and each auxiliary view. In order to see any plane true size, the line of sight for the true-size view must be perpendicular to the edge view of the plane in an adjacent view.

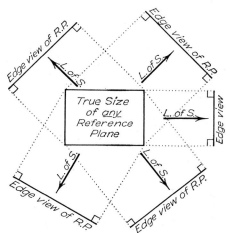

The reference plane upon which *any* view is drawn is true size in that view. In *all* of its *adjacent* views this reference plane will appear in its *edge view* and at 90° to the line of sight (projection lines) between the views.

FIG. 31. Direction of edge view of reference plane.

31. SECONDARY AUXILIARY VIEWS

The auxiliary views projected from a regular view are commonly spoken of as **primary** auxiliary views. In order to draw a primary auxiliary view as has been explained in the previous articles, only two previously drawn views are necessary, and they are usually two of the regular views such as front and top views for an auxiliary view projected off the front view.

A **secondary** auxiliary view is an auxiliary view projected off a primary auxiliary view. As in the case of the primary auxiliary view, only two previously drawn views are necessary in order to draw a secondary auxiliary view. In the case of the secondary auxiliary view, the two previously drawn views are the primary auxiliary view and one of the regular views. In Fig. 32 they are the primary auxiliary view and the top view from which the primary auxiliary view has been projected. The secondary auxiliary view is drawn on an oblique reference plane (*ORP*). In Fig. 32, *ORP* and *HRP* are *both* perpendicular to *ARP*. This is verified by the edge views of *ORP* and *HRP* in the primary auxiliary view where *ARP* is true size. The *ARP* appears in its edge view in the secondary auxiliary view and in the top view. The measurements *along* the projection lines

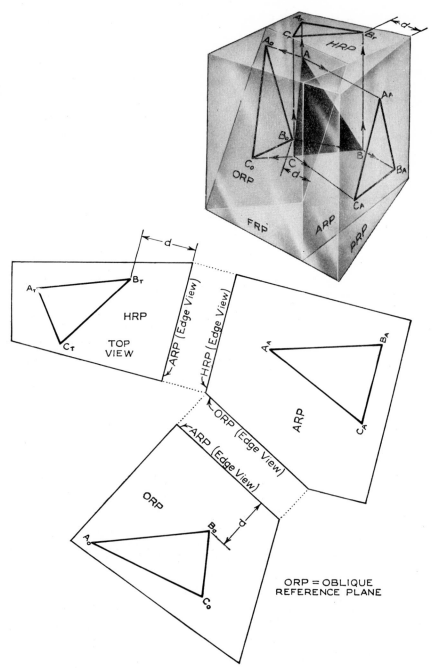

FIG. 32. Secondary auxiliary view.

in the secondary auxiliary view are obtained from the top view and are measured perpendicularly to ARP (in other words, along the projection lines between the top view and the primary auxiliary view). The measurement d obtained from the top view is used to locate point B_O in the secondary auxiliary view. Similar measurements are used to locate points A_O and C_O. *No* measurements for this secondary auxiliary view could have been obtained in the front view and none could have been measured in a horizontal or vertical direction in the top view because they would not have given the correct distances the three points are from ARP.

32. A SERIES OF AUXILIARY VIEWS

Each of a series of auxiliary views is drawn in the same manner that any auxiliary view is drawn. *It should always be remembered that only the two preceding views are used.*

In Fig. 33 the top and front views are given. Auxiliary view 1 is a primary auxiliary view projected off the top view. The top and front views are the two previously drawn views used to draw this view. The top view is the "common" view for view 1 and the front view. View 2 is a secondary auxiliary view, and *only view* 1 *and the top view are used to make this view.* The primary auxiliary view is drawn on ARP which appears in its edge view in both top and auxiliary view 2 views. Measurement e and others parallel to it may be obtained from the top view and used as indicated in view 2.

To understand more clearly how auxiliary view 3 is drawn, the student should cover the front, top, and view 4 with a piece of paper. The front and top views are *not* needed, and view 4 is drawn after view 3 is completed.

View 2 is drawn on the oblique reference plane ORP. ORP will show in its edge view in views 1 and 3. One corner of the object is on ORP and the remainder of the corners are behind this reference plane. View 1 tells how far behind ORP the remaining corners lie. All measurements must be measured parallel to measurement f and perpendicular to ORP. They are to be used in view 3 *along* the projection lines from view 2.

View 3 was drawn on NRP. (The N has no particular significance. K, M, Q, or numerous other letters could have been used.) NRP appears in its edge view in auxiliary views 2 and 4. In Fig. 34 views 2 and 3 and view 4 (which is to be drawn) are separated from the other views of Fig. 33. This was done to show that the front, top, and view 1 views are *not* needed to solve view 4. Dimensions g and g_1 are obtained from view 2 and used in view 4. In both views the dimensions were

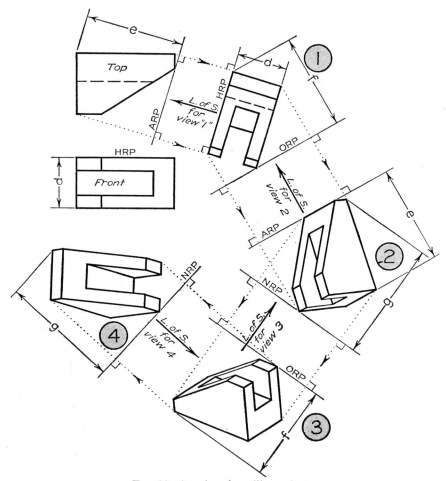

FIG. 33. A series of auxiliary views.

measured perpendicularly to *NRP*. Note that *NRP* is perpendicular to the projection lines between the adjacent views 2 and 3 and views 3 and 4.

33. PROOF THAT ALL AUXILIARY VIEWS ARE PRIMARY

Turn the book counterclockwise until the projection lines between views 2 and 3 are vertical. View 2 then *temporarily* becomes the top view, view 3 becomes the front view, *NRP* becomes *FRP*, *ORP* becomes *HRP*, and view 4 becomes a primary auxiliary view projected off the front view. Any secondary auxiliary view and subsequent auxiliary views may be similarly converted to a primary auxiliary view.

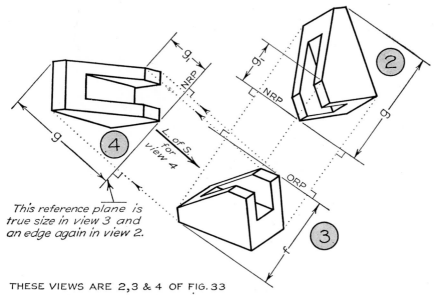

This reference plane is
true size in view 3 and
an edge again in view 2.

THESE VIEWS ARE 2,3 & 4 OF FIG. 33

FIG. 34. How to make one view of a series of auxiliary views.

34. USE OF TRIANGLES AND T SQUARE

Figure 35 shows how parallel and perpendicular lines may be drawn for auxiliary views with two triangles or one triangle and a T square or other straightedge.

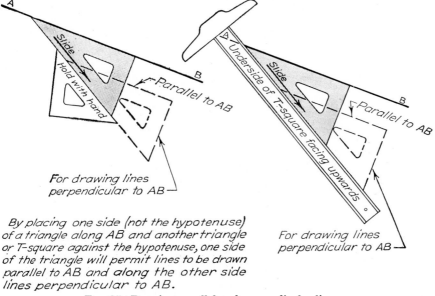

By placing one side (not the hypotenuse)
of a triangle along AB and another triangle
or T-square against the hypotenuse, one side
of the triangle will permit lines to be drawn
parallel to AB and along the other side
lines perpendicular to AB.

FIG. 35. Drawing parallel and perpendicular lines.

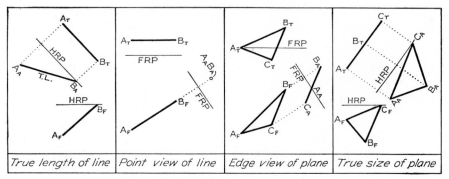

| *True length of line* | *Point view of line* | *Edge view of plane* | *True size of plane* |

FIG. 36. Basic reasons for taking auxiliary views.

35. BASIC REASONS FOR AUXILIARY VIEWS

The basic reasons for all auxiliary views may be divided into four categories (see Fig. 36). It is not uncommon to find the reasons for taking an auxiliary view falling in more than one of the categories.

1. To find the true length of a line.
2. To find the point view of a line.
3. To find the edge view of a plane.
4. To find the true size of a plane.

In finding a plane true size, the center lines of any holes drilled perpendicularly to the plane will appear as points and some surfaces of an object may appear in their edge views in this view.

CHAPTER 5

POINTS AND LINES

36. POINTS ACTUALLY ON LINES

A point actually lying on a line lies on the line in every view of the line. In Fig. 37a point E is on the line AB in all three views and projects orthographically as indicated by the projection lines. If point R is to be on line AB, it must be on the extension of the line in every view.

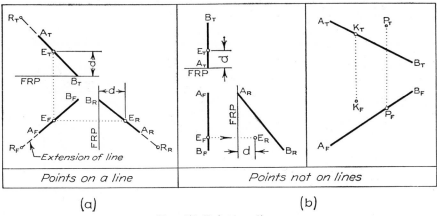

FIG. 37. Points on lines.

37. POINTS APPEARING TO BE ON LINES

In Fig. 37b, E appears to be on line AB in the front and top views, but the side view shows it is not on the line. An auxiliary view of the line and point would have shown the same discrepancy. In the front view point P_F appears to be on line AB. The top view shows that it is directly in back of the line. Point K is directly above the line as the front view indicates.

38. ADDING A POINT TO A LINE

In Fig. 38 point E is projected to an auxiliary view of line AB in order to obtain the elevation measurement d necessary to locate point E_F in the front view. A side view of the line would have given the same solution. See Art. 56 for an alternate solution requiring no auxiliary or side views.

39. SPACE DIRECTIONS

Measurements to the left or right, to the front or rear, and upward or downward (above or below) are each measured *perpendicularly* to a *specified reference plane* (see Fig. 39) and only in a view where that reference plane appears in its edge view. Thus, a point A to be located $\frac{1}{2}$ in. to the rear of another point B must be located by a $\frac{1}{2}$-in. measurement measured perpendicularly to an *FRP* through the other point B. This does *not* mean, however, that the point A must be

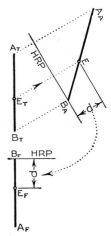

Req'd: To locate the front view of point E on AB.

Fig. 38. Adding a point to a line.

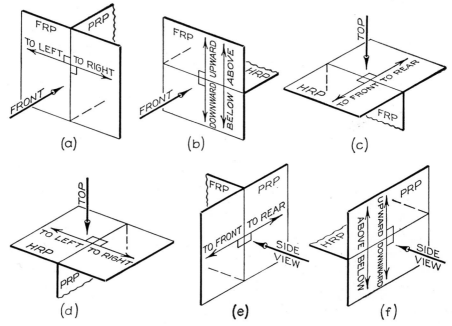

| (a) | (b) | (c) |

| (d) | (e) | (f) |

Measurements to left or right are measured perpendicularly only to PRP
" " to front or rear " " " " " FRP
" " above or below " " " " " HRP

Fig. 39. Space directions.

directly in back of point B. All points $\frac{1}{2}$ in. in back of B will be on a frontal reference plane $\frac{1}{2}$ in. from the FRP containing point B. Thus, if there are no other requirements to locate point A, there are an infinite number of solutions, but all are on the one specified FRP.

40. LOCATING POINTS ON A LINE

Figure 40 locates points M and G on line AB by distances from point B. Point M is somewhere on an FRP $\frac{3}{4}$ in. to the rear of the FRP containing point B. Point M is located on AB where line AB and FRP intersect. Point G is $\frac{1}{2}$ in. to the left of B; thus, it is on a PRP $\frac{1}{2}$ in. to the left of the PRP containing point B. Point G is located where line AB and the PRP $\frac{1}{2}$ in. to the left of B intersect.

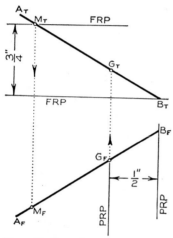

Fig. 40. Locating points on a line.

Alternate solution

Ends of lines should be labelled.

Fig. 41. Label ends of lines.

41. LABELING ENDS OF LINES

All lines (and later planes) should be properly labeled. Figure 41 shows two side-view possibilities because the top and front views of the line were not labeled.

42. INTERSECTING AND NONINTERSECTING LINES

The point of intersection of two lines which actually intersect will project from view to view as indicated in Fig. 42a. Lines crossing each other in a single or, in some cases, two views are not necessarily intersecting lines. Figure 42b shows two examples of nonintersecting lines.

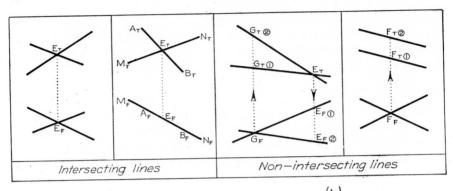

Intersecting lines   Non–intersecting lines

(a)   (b)

FIG. 42. Intersecting and nonintersecting lines.

There are two positions of point G_T in the top view and two positions of point E_F in the front view. The two positions of point F_T are on lines which appear to be parallel. (They are not parallel in space, however.)

In Fig. 43 lines AB and MN apparently intersect, since the point E_T can apparently be projected onto both lines in the front view. The side view (an auxiliary view would show the same result) shows that they do not intersect because there are two E_R positions.

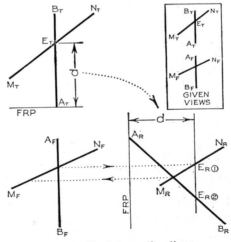

FIG. 43. Nonintersecting lines.

In Fig. 44 the two lines AB and MN intersect by placing the intersection point E on *both* lines. E_T projected to the front view of line MN gives a second point on the line $A_F B_F$. The extension of the line connecting these two points in the front view locates B_F.

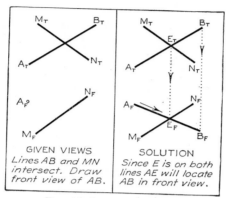

FIG. 44. Intersecting lines.

43. PARALLEL LINES

Lines which are parallel in space will appear parallel in *all* orthographic views and axonometric* drawings. Lines may appear parallel in a given view or two and still not appear parallel in all views (see Fig. 45).

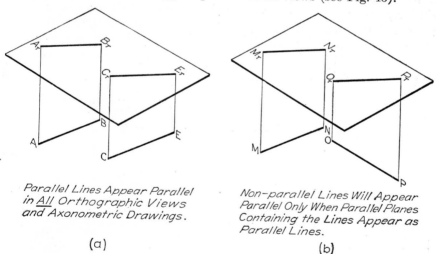

Parallel Lines Appear Parallel in All Orthographic Views and Axonometric Drawings.

(a)

Non-parallel Lines Will Appear Parallel Only When Parallel Planes Containing the Lines Appear as Parallel Lines.

(b)

FIG. 45. Parallel and nonparallel lines.

* Axonometric drawings include isometric, dimetric, and trimetric drawings.

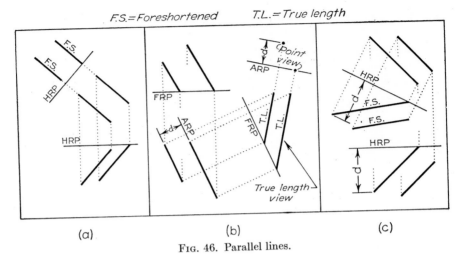

FIG. 46. Parallel lines.

In Fig. 46 are three examples of parallel lines. The uneven lengths of the lines do *not* affect the parallelism. When one parallel line appears as a point, the other one will also appear as a point.

In Fig. 47, *AB* and *CE* appear parallel in both top and side views of both examples. Yet one pair is parallel and the other pair is not. The front views proved that which the top and side views could not conclusively prove. Edge views of parallel planes (*FRP*) containing these two sets of lines make both sets of lines appear parallel in the top and side views. The two *FRP* planes containing the two lines of each example appear as planes in the front view, thereby proving one pair to be parallel and the other pair not parallel.

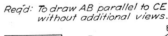

Req'd: To draw AB parallel to CE without additional views.

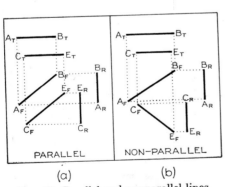

FIG. 47. Parallel and nonparallel lines.

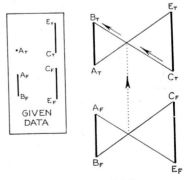

FIG. 48. Parallel lines.

Figure 48 shows how the top view of AB may be drawn without additional views. Since intersecting lines and parallel lines create a plane, the top view of AB may be found by using the intersecting lines as indicated on the drawing.

44. TRUE LENGTHS OF LINES

The true length of any line appears in a view where the line of sight for that view is perpendicular to the line. All frontal lines are true length in the front view because the line of sight for the front view is perpendicular to all frontal lines. In Fig. 49 the auxiliary plane is parallel to the line AB and the line of sight for that auxiliary view is perpendicular to the line and the plane. Thus, the line will appear true length in the auxiliary view.

The line AB of Fig. 50 is true length in the auxiliary view because the line of sight for the auxiliary view is perpendicular to the line as the top view indicates. The pencil is likewise true length. The true length of AB could have been obtained in an auxiliary view projected off the front view, side view, or any auxiliary view of the line provided the line of sight was made perpendicular to the line.

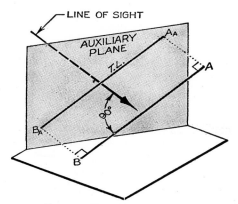

FIG. 49. True length of a line.

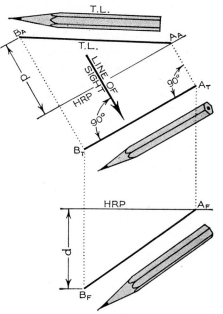

FIG. 50. True length of a line.

In solving for the true lengths of segments of bent rods (see Fig. 51), piping, or tubing, base them on the portion of the center lines between the intersections of the center lines as A and B.

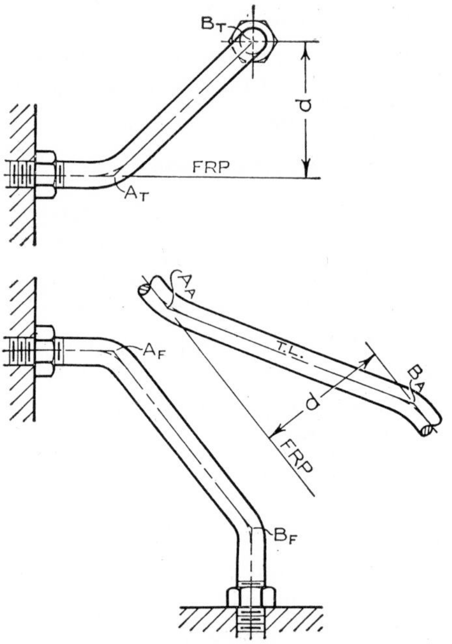

45. PERPENDICULAR LINES

Two lines which are perpendicular to each other in space will have the 90° relationship show in an orthographic view when either of the following two conditions exist:

1. When both lines are true length.

2. When only one line is true length.

Two lines may be perpendicular to each other in space and *not* intersect.

In Fig. 52a the 90° relationship of the two mutually perpendicular edges of the triangle shows in the front view because both edges are true length.   In Fig. 52b the 90° relationship shows in both front and top views because one edge is true length in both views.   In Fig. 52c the 90° relationship between the same two edges of the triangle does not show because neither edge is true length in either front or top view.

Fig. 51. Application of true length of a line.

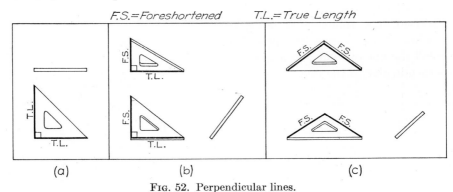

F.S.=Foreshortened   T.L.=True Length

(a)   (b)   (c)

Fig. 52. Perpendicular lines.

The small square at the vertex of the angle of the two perpendicular
lines in Fig. 52*a* and *b* is used to denote 90° between the lines in those
views.   It may be used whenever two lines appear perpendicular in a
view although they may or may not be perpendicular in space.

In Fig. 53 line *PO* is perpendicular to lines *AB*, *CE*, and *DG* and will
appear perpendicular to each of them in the top view because it is true
length.   Only *AB* of the three lines perpendicular to *PO* is true length
in the top view.

BC is perpendicular to *RB* in space, and they appear perpendicular in
the top view because *BC* is true length.   *BE* also appears perpendicular
to *RB* in the top view, but they are *not* perpendicular to each other in
space.   Although both *RB* and *BE* are foreshortened in the top view,
they can still appear perpendicular to each other in a given view.

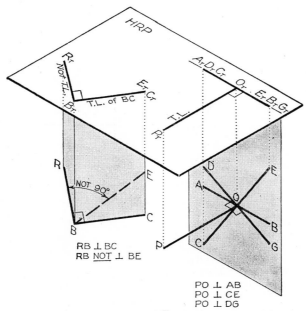

*Two lines perpendicular in space will <u>appear</u> perpend-
icular in a given view if either or both lines are true
length. If both lines are foreshortened they will <u>not</u>
appear perpendicular. Two foreshortened lines may
appear perpendicular in a given view but will <u>not</u>
be perpendicular in space. Example $R_T B_T$ and $B_T E_T$.*

Fig. 53. Perpendicular and nonperpendicular lines.

An application of perpendicular lines is shown in Fig. 54, where the true-length major axis of the ellipse view of the base is perpendicular to the axis of the right circular cone. The same is true for a right circular cylinder or any right circular object. This is *not* true for oblique circular objects.

Figure 55 shows that two lines may appear perpendicular to each other in two views and still not be perpendicular in space. If the lines were perpendicular in space, *CE* would have to appear perpendicular to the true-length view of *AB*. Both *AB* and *CE* are foreshortened in the front and top views.

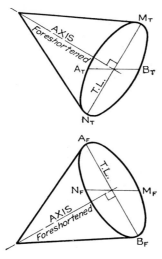

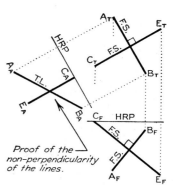

FIG. 55. Nonperpendicular lines appearing to be perpendicular.

The axis in space is perpendicular to all diameter lines of the base of a right circular cone or cylinder, but when the axis shows foreshortened in an orthographic view it appears perpendicular to only one diameter line.

FIG. 54. Application of perpendicular lines.

46. POINT VIEW OF A LINE

In order to find the point view of a line, the line of sight for the view must be taken parallel to the line. In order to do this, first the line must be found in its true length as is shown in Fig. 56. The true-length view of AB could have been obtained in a view projected off the front view. The line of sight for the secondary auxiliary view as indicated is parallel to the *true-length view* of AB. This illustration also shows line AB to be the line of intersection of two planes.

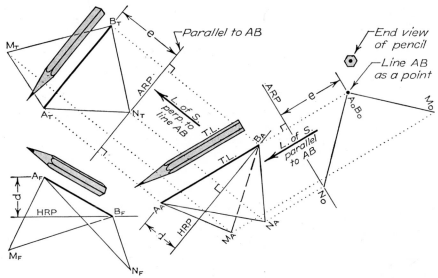

FIG. 56. Point view of a line.

47. COMMON PERPENDICULAR TO TWO SKEW LINES

The common perpendicular to two skew (nonparallel, nonperpendicular, nonintersecting) lines involves the double application of perpendicular lines, since the common perpendicular must be perpendicular to both lines. The method of solution shown in Figs. 57 and 58 is based on finding the point view of either line. CE appears in its point view on the picture plane. The common perpendicular PO will appear true length in this view, and since it is to be perpendicular in space to AB, it will appear perpendicular to AB. (When either of two perpendicular lines

appears in its point view, the other line will appear true length.) The
drawing of the common perpendicular through the point view of *CE*
perpendicular to *AB* will locate point *P*, which is one end of the common

perpendicular. In the true-length
view of *CE*, the common perpendicular may be drawn perpendicular to the true-length view of *CE*
through the previously located
point *P*. Thus, two views of the
common perpendicular are found
and others may be obtained by
regular projection.

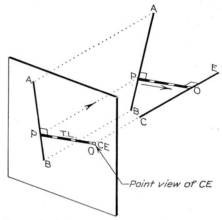

There are several other methods
of determining the single line which
is the common perpendicular to two
skew lines. Two methods involving planes are explained in Arts. 73
and 74.

Fig. 57. Common perpendicular to two
skew lines.

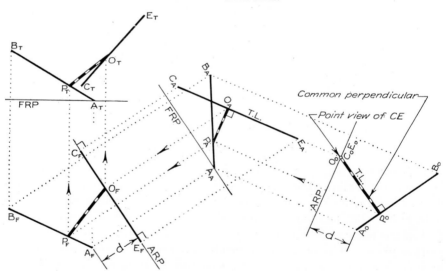

Fig. 58. Common perpendicular to two skew lines.

48. SLOPE OF A LINE

See Art. 81 for slope of a line.

LINES AND PLANES

49. ADDING LINES TO A PLANE

Any line intersecting two lines of a plane or intersecting one line and parallel to another line of the plane lies in the plane. In Fig. 59*b* line *AB* was extended until it intersected two lines of the plane; then the two points of intersection were projected to the top view. The top view of the line *AB* was drawn through the projected two points of intersection. In Fig. 59*c* two lines of the plane as well as *AB* were extended until two intersection points were obtained. The two intersection points were then projected to the front view. Line *AB* extended contains these

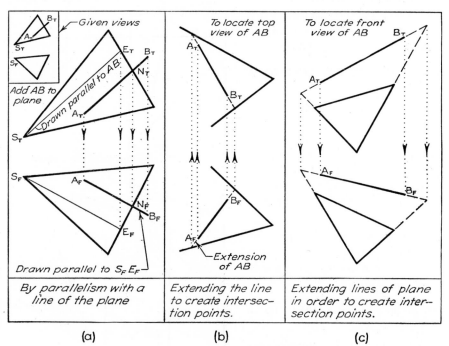

By parallelism with a line of the plane	Extending the line to create intersection points.	Extending lines of plane in order to create intersection points.
(a)	(b)	(c)

FIG. 59. Adding lines to planes.

two intersection points in the front view. In Fig. 59a line *AB* was added to the plane by first adding line *SE* to the plane and drawing it parallel to the top view of *AB*. Then the front view of *AB* will be parallel to $S_F E_F$ and will contain the single intersection point N_F where *AB* intersects one line of the plane.

50. ADDING HORIZONTAL LINES TO A PLANE

The line of intersection of an *HRP* with the plane *ABC* of Fig. 60 is a horizontal line. *All* horizontal lines of an oblique plane are parallel. A horizontal line may be added to a plane by making it parallel to *HRP* and projecting its intersections with two other lines of the plane to other views (see Fig. 63a).

51. ADDING FRONTAL LINES TO A PLANE

A frontal line of a plane is the intersection of an *FRP* with the plane *ABC* as shown in Fig. 61. *All* frontal lines of an oblique plane are parallel to each other. A frontal line may be added to a plane by making it parallel to the *FRP* in an edge view of this reference plane and then projecting its intersections with other lines of the plane to other views (see Fig. 63b).

52. ADDING PROFILE LINES TO A PLANE

A profile line of a plane is parallel to *PRP*, and it may be considered as the line of intersec-

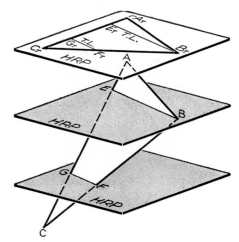

Fig. 60. Horizontal lines on a plane.

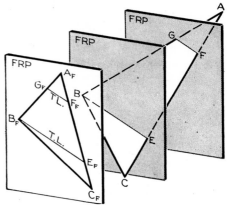

Fig. 61. Frontal lines on a plane.

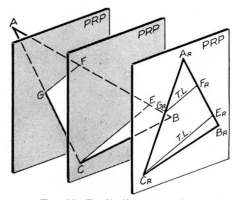

Fig. 62. Profile lines on a plane.

tion of *PRP* with the plane *ABC* of Fig. 62. A profile line may be added to a plane by making the line parallel to *PRP* and having it intersect two other lines of the plane. These intersections may be projected from view to view as shown in Fig. 63c.

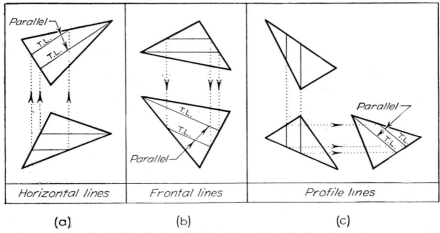

Horizontal lines	Frontal lines	Profile lines
(a)	(b)	(c)

Fig. 63. Adding horizontal, frontal, and profile lines to a plane.

53. ADDING POINTS TO A PLANE

To add a point to a plane, add a line containing the point to the plane. The line may need to be extended as was done in order to add point *R* to the plane shown in Fig. 64.

54. REPLACING LINES INCONVENIENT TO USE

Two methods are given in Fig. 65 showing how to avoid using line *AB*. Points between *A* and *B* are difficult to locate. Point *A* of line *AB* is definitely located in all views and may be used. Extend $B_T C_T$ to find point E_T, which will be on a frontal line through point A_T of the plane. The desired frontal line through *C* may then be drawn parallel to $A_F E_F$ through point C_F in the front view.

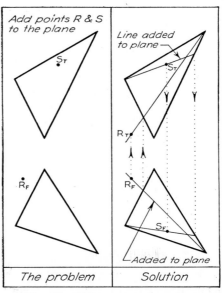

The problem	Solution

Fig. 64. Adding points to a plane.

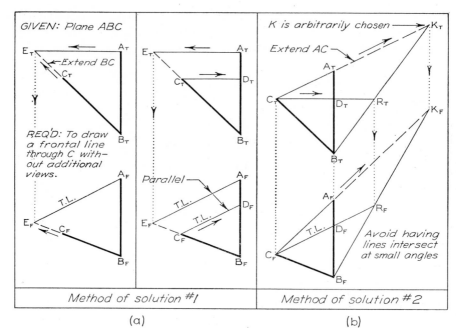

FIG. 65. Replacing a line inconvenient to use.

The second solution is the extension of line AC and arbitrarily choosing point K. Graphical accuracy requires that the angle in the top view between the lines $C_T R_T$ and $R_T B_T$ should be not less than 30° (see Fig. 332), and in the front view, the angle between the vertical projection line and $B_F K_F$ should likewise be not less than 30°. $C_T D_T$ extended will locate R_T on line $B_T K_T$. The front view of point R on line BK will establish the front view of the frontal line through C and point D_F.

55. IS IT A PLANE?

Two nonparallel lines not intersecting within the limits of the paper may or may not represent a plane. Connecting the ends of

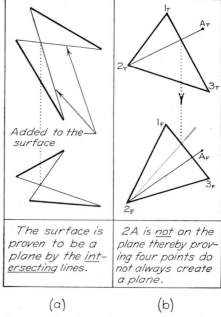

FIG. 66. Proving the existence of a plane.

the lines or *other points* of the lines as shown in Fig. 66*a* will determine whether the two original lines constitute a plane. Only if the added lines intersect does a plane exist. Graphical accuracy requires as large angles as possible between the added lines in both views (see Fig. 333).

Four points do not always determine a plane. For example, the fourth point *A* is not on a line of the plane of the other three points of Fig. 66*b*. The line *A*2 is not on the plane.

An application of this proof as to whether a plane exists is shown in Fig. 67. Careless draftsmanship produced a drawing from which a die was made according to given dimensions at considerable expense, only to find out later that the furnace brick would not mate with the next brick. The cost of the *delay* added to the expense. This is only one example of many proving that it pays to know fundamentals.

FURNACE BRICK

This furnace brick was made by a Saint Louis concern from the drawing of another concern. The drawing was incorrectly drawn and dimensioned accordingly. The surface A to F was proven by the method here shown not to be a plane; thus it did not match with its mating brick.

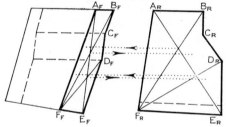

Since lines AE, BF & DF connecting corners of the surface do not intersect, the surface is not a plane.

FIG. 67. Proving the existence of a plane.

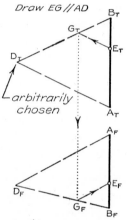

Draw *EG // AD*

Req'd: To locate the front view of point E on AB without additional views.

FIG. 68. Plane method of adding a point to a line.

56. ADDING A POINT TO A LINE (Plane Method)

A third point *D* arbitrarily chosen will, with line *AB* of Fig. 68, constitute a plane. A line through E_T parallel to either *AD* or *BD* will be on the plane. The front view of this added parallel line will locate E_F on *AB*.

57. EDGE VIEW OF A PLANE

The edge view of any plane may be obtained by looking parallel with *any* line of the plane. By looking parallel with a line of the plane, you will see the line in its point view and the plane in its edge view through the point view of the line. If the line is an oblique line, the true length of the line would first have to be obtained in an auxiliary view. A frontal, horizontal, or profile line added to the plane will be true length in one of the regular views. Any one of these true-length lines would eliminate

drawing an auxiliary view in order to find a line true length. In Fig. 69 a horizontal line (it should be made as long as possible for greater accuracy) is added to plane *ABC*. Since all horizontal lines are true length in the top view, the horizontal line will appear in its point view in an auxiliary view whose line of sight has been taken parallel to it. The plane will then appear in its edge view and contain the point view of the horizontal line. As a precaution against inaccuracies as well as errors, it is safest to project

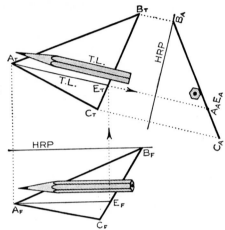

FIG. 69. Edge view of a plane.

more than one point of the plane in addition to the point view of the line. If the plane is correctly drawn in its edge view, each and every point of the plane will coincide with that edge view.

58. TRUE SIZE OF A PLANE

The true-size view of a plane is obtained by looking (line of sight) perpendicularly at the edge view of the plane. The horizontal plane is true size in the top view because the line of sight for that view is perpendicular in the front view to the edge view of that plane. An inclined plane is true size in a primary auxiliary view because the plane is in its edge view in one of the regular views. The line of sight for the auxiliary view will appear perpendicular to the edge view of the inclined plane in the regular view (see Fig. 73). An oblique plane must *first* be found in its edge view as shown in Fig. 70. Since the profile line is true length in the side view, the line of sight for the edge view of the plane *ABC* will be taken parallel to this line. The true size of the plane will show in the secondary auxiliary view when the line of sight for that view is perpendicular to the edge view of the plane.

Practical applications of fundamentals are frequently obscured by the requirements, the descriptive terms, and names of the individual parts of the application. This is illustrated in Fig. 71, where the angle at which the pipes are to be cut off is the *desired* result. The desired result will be obtained only when the plane of the center lines of the pipes is found true

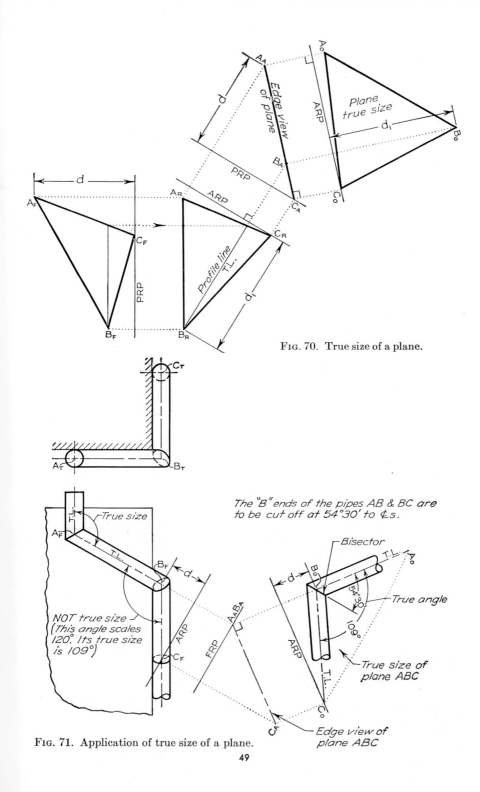

FIG. 70. True size of a plane.

The "B" ends of the pipes AB & BC are to be cut off at 54°30' to ℄s.

FIG. 71. Application of true size of a plane.

49

size.   The center lines of the pipes are not ordinarily thought of as edges or lines of a plane.   Thus, the student must *learn to recognize* applications of the fundamentals.   When the plane ABC (Fig. 71) of the center lines is obtained true size, the desired angle may be measured by bisecting the angle $A_oB_oC_o$.   It is obvious that bisecting the 120° angle of the front view or the 90° angle of the top view would not have produced the correct result of 54°30'.

59. TRUE AND FALSE BISECTORS OF AN ANGLE

Figure 72 shows how the bisector of an angle is obtained.   Both sides of the angle must be true length.   The bisecting of an angle in a view where the plane of the angle is foreshortened always produces a *false* bisector with but one exception.   The exception is when both sides of the angle have the same ratio of foreshortening, and usually it is not known at what ratio each line of a plane foreshortens.

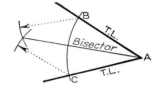

$AB = AC$ and both must be true length

FIG. 72. Bisecting an angle.

The true bisector of the angle MNO of Fig. 73 obtained from the auxiliary view where the plane of the angle is true size is compared with the false bisector obtained by bisecting the top view of the foreshortened plane of the angle.   The uneven sides of the top view of the angle are shown by their true lengths $N1$ and $N2$.

60. VISIBILITY OF LINES AND PLANES

When two lines cross in a given view, a question of visibility is involved unless the two lines intersect.   Since lines RS and AB of Fig. 74 do not intersect, one line is visible at point E on the reference plane while the other line is invisible.   There are two points designated as E with one on each line.   By looking along the line of sight, E_1, which

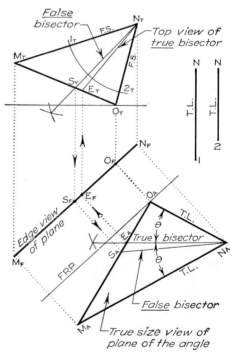

FIG. 73. True and false bisectors of an angle.

is on RS, is seen first, thus making RS instead of line AB visible in that view. The visibility of one line relative to the other may or may not change in the next view of the two lines.

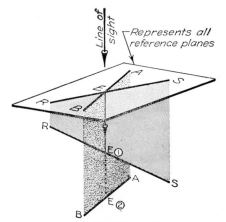

FIG. 74. Visibility of lines.

In Fig. 75a the visibility of a line with a plane is based upon the visibility of the line relative to the visibility of the *individual* lines of the plane that it crosses in a given view. Line M_TN_T is visible in the top view relative to line B_TC_T of the plane, while it is invisible relative to line A_TC_T of the same plane in the same view. G_{F1} of line A_TC_T is higher than G_{F2} of line M_TN_T as shown in the front view; thus line A_TC_T is visible in the top view rather than M_TN_T at that point. The visibility of the line changes at the piercing point (PP) of the line with the plane.

The visibility of the rods in Fig. 75b is determined by the visibility of their center lines provided the rods do not intersect. Rod MN is visible

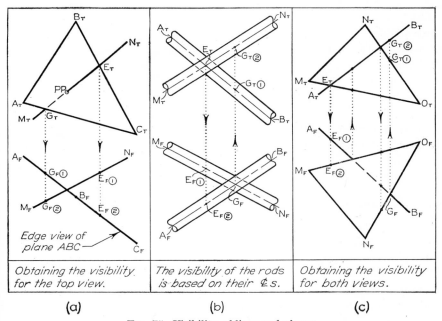

Obtaining the visibility for the top view.	The visibility of the rods is based on their ℄s.	Obtaining the visibility for both views.
(a)	(b)	(c)

FIG. 75. Visibility of lines and planes.

in the top view relative to rod AB, but the visibility is reversed in the front view. G_{T1} being closer to the front than G_{T2} makes rod AB visible in the front view.

In Fig. 75c line AB is visible in the top view relative to both of the lines of the plane MNO that it crosses. Thus, the line does not pierce the plane within the limits of the triangle as line MN of Fig. 75a pierced the plane ABC.

The visibility of one plane relative to another is likewise determined by the visibility of individual lines of one plane relative to individual lines of the other plane. The points where lines of one plane cross lines of the other plane should be considered on the basis of an *individual* line crossing another line. Line 2_F3_F of Fig. 76 crosses C_FA_F. Which line is visible at point F_F depends on whether F_{T1} is on line 2_T3_T or C_TA_T. Since it is on line 2_T3_T, then line 2_F3_F is visible in the front view. Line A_FC_F will be invisible within the limits of the triangle $1_F2_F3_F$ until it reaches the line of intersection of the two planes. The same reasoning may be applied to the other lines which cross in each view.

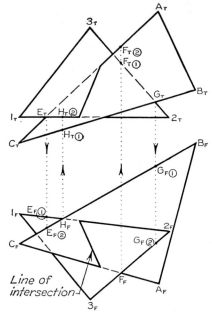

FIG. 76. Visibility of planes.

61. A LINE PARALLEL TO A PLANE

A line parallel to a plane must be parallel to a line of the plane. The given line, depending upon the conditions of the problem, will be parallel to either a given line of the plane or a line to be added to

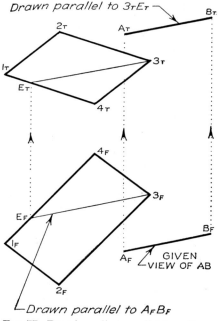

FIG. 77. Drawing a line parallel to a plane.

the plane. In order to make line AB of Fig. 77 parallel to the plane 1-2-3-4, a line $3_F E_F$ should be drawn parallel to the given front view of AB. The top view of AB should be drawn parallel to the top view of line $3E$, thereby making line AB parallel to the plane because it is parallel to a line of the plane. In order to determine the direction of a line parallel to two intersecting planes, fold a piece of paper, but do not close the fold. Then with a pencil representing a line which is parallel to both planes of the folded paper, determine the direction the line (pencil) must be to be parallel to both planes.

62. A PLANE PARALLEL TO A LINE

A plane to be parallel to a line must have a line on the plane parallel to the given line. Figure 78a shows the construction of a plane which contains the given line RS and is drawn parallel to the given line AB. Figure 79 shows the construction of plane MNO drawn parallel to the two skew lines AB and CE. The plane MNO was formed by drawing MN parallel to AB and NO parallel to CE. An orthographic solution is

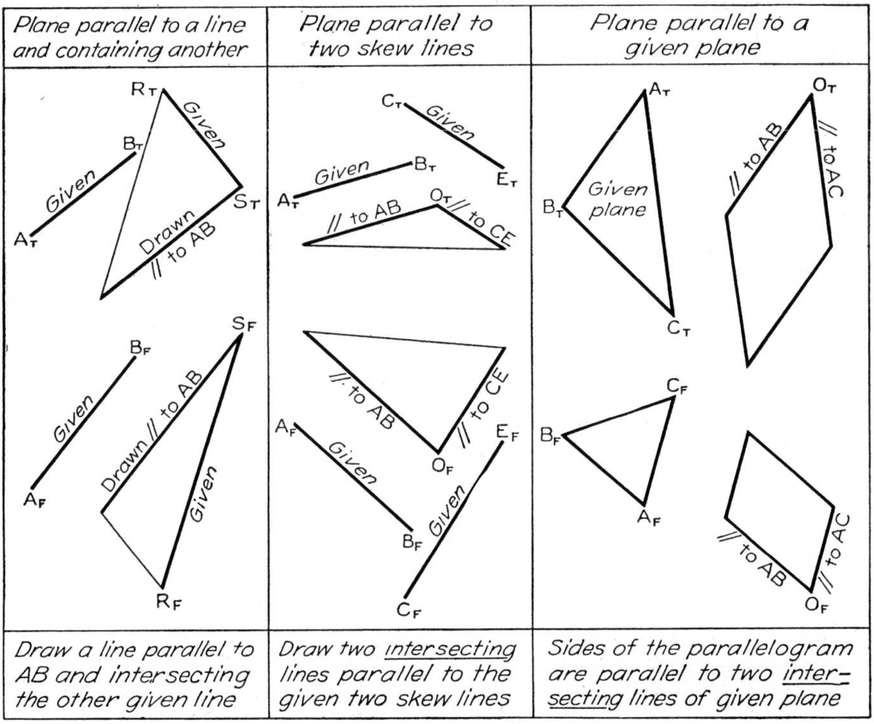

Plane parallel to a line and containing another	Plane parallel to two skew lines	Plane parallel to a given plane
Draw a line parallel to AB and intersecting the other given line	Draw two <u>intersecting</u> lines parallel to the given two skew lines	Sides of the parallelogram are parallel to two <u>intersecting</u> lines of given plane
(a)	(b)	(c)

Fig. 78. Planes parallel to lines and planes.

shown in Fig. 78b where a plane has been constructed through point O parallel to the skew lines AB and CE.

63. PARALLEL PLANES

Two planes to be definitely parallel must have two *intersecting* lines of one plane parallel to *intersecting* lines of the other plane. In Fig. 78c the plane constructed through point O parallel to the plane ABC has been formed by two intersecting

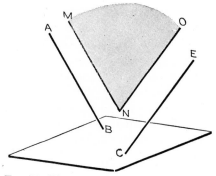

FIG. 79. Plane parallel to two skew lines.

lines drawn parallel to two intersecting lines AB and AC of plane ABC.

In Fig. 80a the plane $ABCE$ is represented by parallel lines. In order definitely to establish a plane through O parallel to this plane, the line BE is added so that the new plane can be represented by *intersecting* lines which are parallel to *intersecting* lines of plane $ABCE$.

In Fig. 80b the two planes appear parallel in the top and front views

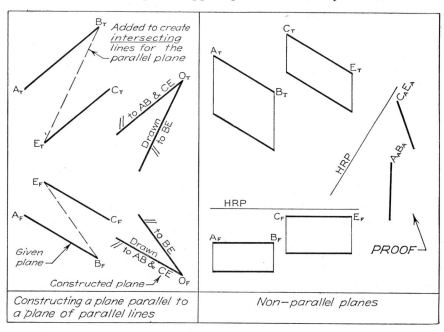

(a)   (b)

FIG. 80. Parallel and nonparallel planes.

because of the parallelism of the horizontal lines of the parallelograms. The edge view of the planes in the auxiliary view shows that they are *not* parallel.

64. PROVING WHETHER PLANES ARE PARALLEL

Planes represented by different geometric outlines may be parallel. The proof that the planes are not parallel in Fig. 81 does *not* lie in the fact that one plane is represented by a triangle and the other by a parallelogram. Line *CG* drawn parallel to line 2-3 in the one view is found to be parallel to 2-3 in the next view. This proves *only* that the planes *may* be parallel. If line *CG* had not been parallel to 2-3 in the next view, the planes would definitely not be parallel. Line A_TE_T which was drawn parallel to 3_T4_T in the top view is found in the front view not to be parallel to 3_F4_F; thus the planes are not parallel.

A plane containing two parallel lines may have these two parallel lines parallel to two parallel lines of another plane and the planes not parallel as in Fig. 82. The two sets of parallel lines are parallel to the line of intersection of the two planes. Parallel pairs of *intersecting* lines are necessary to establish parallel planes *definitely*.

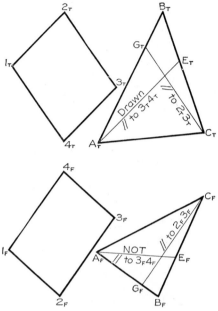

Since A_TE_T is parallel to 3_T4_T and A_FE_F is *not* parallel to 3_F4_F the planes are *not* parallel. The line of intersection of the two planes is parallel to 2,3 and C,G

FIG. 81. Checking whether planes are parallel.

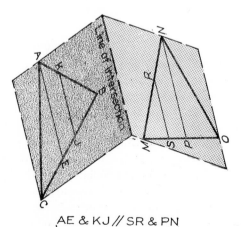

AE & KJ // SR & PN

They are also parallel to the line of intersection of the two planes.

FIG. 82. (*Right*) Parallel lines of intersecting planes.

65. A LINE PERPENDICULAR TO A PLANE (Auxiliary-view Method)

A line perpendicular to a plane will appear perpendicular to the edge view of the plane.   The line will also be *true length* in the *same* view.   In Fig. 83 line MN appears perpendicular to the edge view of plane 1-2-3-4 in the auxiliary view.   The side view of $M_R N_R$ must be perpendicular to the line of sight (projection lines) for the auxiliary view; otherwise line MN could not be true length in the auxiliary view.

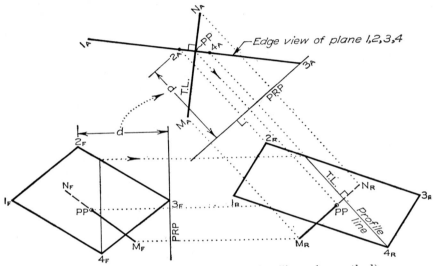

FIG. 83. Line perpendicular to a plane (auxiliary-view method).

66. A LINE PERPENDICULAR TO A PLANE (Perpendicular to True-length Lines of the Plane Method)

A line in space is perpendicular to every line of the plane, and the lines of the plane need not intersect the perpendicular line.   However, the line perpendicular to the plane will appear perpendicular in a given view *only* to those lines of the plane appearing *true length* (see Art. 45).   In the regular views these true-length lines will be the horizontal, frontal, or profile lines of the plane.   This is illustrated in Fig. 84, where line MN appears in the front perpendicular to *all* the frontal lines of the plane and in the top view to *all* the horizontal lines of the plane.   Note in the pictorial of the line and plane that the line pierces the plane at PP and only one frontal and one horizontal line pass through the piercing point.

In Fig. 85 the perpendicular line AB appears perpendicular to the several frontal lines, but the crossing points of this line with the several frontal lines do *not* locate the piercing point.   The method of obtaining the piercing point is explained in Arts. 69 to 71.   The perpendicular line

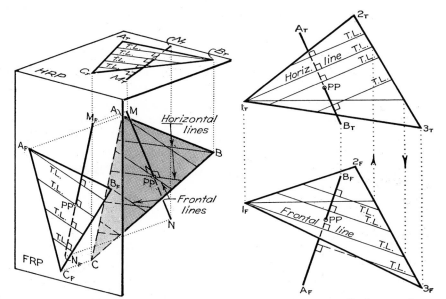

FIG. 84. Line perpendicular to a plane.   FIG. 85. Line perpendicular to a plane.

AB appears perpendicular to the true-length horizontal lines of the top view.

A line perpendicular to a plane must be perpendicular to at least two *intersecting* lines of the plane. Line AB is not perpendicular to the plane solely because it is perpendicular to several frontal *or* horizontal lines. It is perpendicular to the plane because the frontal *and* horizontal lines *intersect* and the line AB is perpendicular to all frontal and horizontal lines of the plane. A line may be perpendicular to the horizontal lines of a plane and lie in the plane but would not in this case be perpendicular to the frontal lines of the plane.

In Fig. 86 line 1-2 is perpendicular to the plane ABC because it is perpendicular to two *intersecting* true-length lines even though one of them is true length in an auxiliary view.

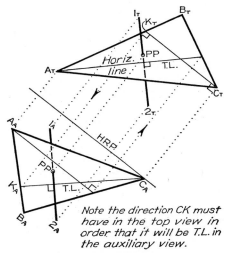

Note the direction CK must
have in the top view in
order that it will be T.L. in
the auxiliary view.

FIG. 86. Line perpendicular to a plane.

67. A PLANE PERPENDICULAR TO A LINE

A plane perpendicular to a line is the converse of a line perpendicular to a plane. A line is determined perpendicular to a plane by making it perpendicular to *intersecting* frontal and horizontal or frontal and profile lines of the plane. A plane perpendicular to a line may be represented by two *intersecting* horizontal and frontal or frontal and profile lines.

In Fig. 87 the plane perpendicular to the line AB at point B has its true-length frontal line MN perpendicular to the front view of AB and the true-length horizontal line 1-2 perpendicular to the top view of AB.

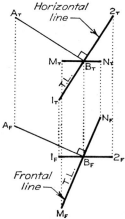

Fig. 87. Plane perpendicular to a line.

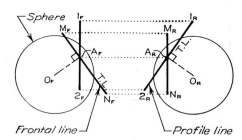

A plane tangent to a sphere is perpendicular to the radial line through the point of tangency.

Fig. 88. Plane perpendicular to a line.

Figure 88 shows the construction of a plane tangent to a sphere at point A. The plane may be drawn perpendicular to the radial line AO of the sphere. The true-length frontal line MN has been drawn perpendicular to AO in the front view, and the true-length profile line perpendicular to AO in the side view. See Art. 135 for another method of obtaining the same plane.

68. PERPENDICULAR PLANES

To draw a plane perpendicular to *another* plane, one line of either plane must be perpendicular to the other plane. A plane perpendicular to *two* planes must be perpendicular to the line of intersection of the two planes.

69. PIERCING POINTS OF A LINE WITH A PLANE (Auxiliary-view Method)

The piercing point of any line with a plane may be found in *any* view (usually it is an auxiliary view) where the plane appears in its edge view. Plane 1-2-3 of Fig. 89 appears in its edge view in the auxiliary view. The piercing point is where the auxiliary view of line AB crosses the edge view of the plane. Since the piercing point is on the line AB, it may be projected from view to view as a part of AB.

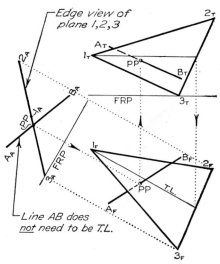

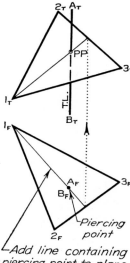

FIG. 89. Piercing point of a line with a plane.

FIG. 90. Piercing point of a line with a plane.

70. PIERCING POINT OF A LINE WITH A PLANE (Point-view-of-line Method)

The point view of the line will contain the piercing point of the line with the plane.   The point view of the line may be in a regular view as in Fig. 90 or in an auxiliary view.   Add a convenient line containing the point view of the given line to the plane.   The piercing point will be found in an adjacent view where the added line and the given line AB intersect.

71. PIERCING POINT OF A LINE WITH A PLANE (Plane Perpendicular to Reference Plane Method)

A cutting plane which is taken perpendicular to a reference plane and contains the given line will intersect the given plane.   The piercing point will be where the line of intersection of the two planes intersects the given line.   In Fig. 91a the indicated cutting plane *containing* the given line AB is perpendicular to HRP and will appear in its edge view in the top view.   The cutting plane intersects plane RST along line LI.   Since LI and AB lie in the *same* plane (the cutting plane), the piercing point will be where these two lines intersect, which is PP. PP is on lines AB and LI, and LI is on plane RST, but AB is not; thus PP is the *only* point that can be on the line and the plane.

Figure 91b shows that the *same* piercing point could have been obtained by making the cutting plane perpendicular to *FRP*. Whichever cutting plane is more convenient to use is the cutting plane to use. The cutting plane can also be taken perpendicular to an *ARP* to obtain the same piercing point.

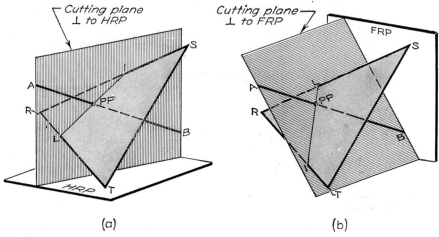

FIG. 91. Piercing point of a line with a plane (cutting-plane method).

In Fig. 92 the edge view of a cutting plane perpendicular to *HRP* is shown in the top view. Lines 4-3 and 1-2 pierce the edge view of the cutting plane at PP_1 and PP_2. The line of intersection of this plane with plane 1-2-3-4 is the line connecting PP_1 with PP_2 in the front view.

In Fig. 93a the top view of line *AB* is *assumed* to be the edge view of a cutting plane perpendicular to *HRP*. $R_T S_T$ pierces the cutting plane at L_T, and $S_T T_T$ pierces it at I_T. $L_F I_F$ is the line of intersection of the cutting plane with plane *RST*. The piercing point is where $L_F I_F$ intersects $A_F B_F$.

In Fig. 93b the same problem was solved by *assuming* the front view of *AB* to be the edge view of a cutting plane perpendicular to *FRP*. The same piercing point is found where $L_T I_T$ intersects with $A_T B_T$.

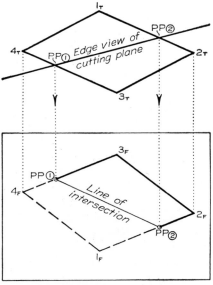

FIG. 92. Intersection of cutting plane with given plane.

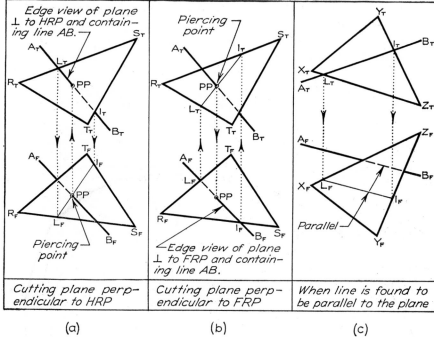

Cutting plane perpendicular to HRP	Cutting plane perpendicular to FRP	When line is found to be parallel to the plane
(a)	(b)	(c)

Fig. 93. Piercing point of a line with a plane.

In Fig. 93c the cutting plane taken perpendicular to HRP contains the top view of AB. The line of intersection $L_F I_F$ of the cutting plane with plane XYZ was found to be parallel to $A_F B_F$. The parallelism proves that line AB is parallel to plane XYZ.

72. PROJECTING A LINE PERPENDICULARLY ONTO ANY PLANE

A line to be projected perpendicularly onto any plane is projected by two lines perpendicular to the plane. The projection of the line onto the plane is the line connecting the two piercing points of the two projectors with the plane. As Fig. 94 shows, the top view of the line AB has been obtained by two projectors through points A and B drawn perpendicularly to HRP. The top view of the line is the line connecting the two piercing points A_T and B_T. A line can be projected onto any plane and is obtained in the same manner.

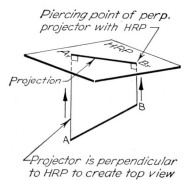

Fig. 94. Projecting a line perpendicularly onto a plane.

Figure 95 shows pictorially the projection of line AB onto plane MNO using two projectors perpendicular to plane MNO. The projection is the line connecting the two piercing points $A_{\text{PROJ}}B_{\text{PROJ}}$. The piercing point of the line AB with the plane MNO is the intersection of the extensions of the lines AB and $A_{\text{PROJ}}B_{\text{PROJ}}$. The piercing point of line AB with the plane MNO would have been between points A_{PROJ} and B_{PROJ} if A and B had been on opposite sides of the plane MNO.

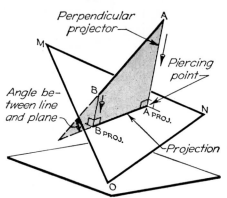

Fig. 95. Projecting a line perpendicularly onto a plane.

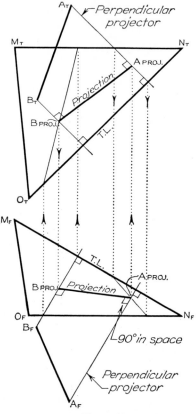

Fig. 96. Projecting a line perpendicularly onto a plane.

Figure 96 shows orthographically the projection of line AB onto plane MNO. The projectors were drawn perpendicular to two intersecting true-length lines. The piercing points were obtained by cutting planes containing the projectors of which one cutting plane is perpendicular to HRP and the other perpendicular to FRP.

73. COMMON PERPENDICULAR TO TWO SKEW LINES (Line-and-Plane Method)

The line-and-plane method of locating the common perpendicular to two skew lines is based on the relationship of a line perpendicular to a plane. The plane is to contain one skew line and be parallel to the other skew line. When the plane is true size, the common perpendicular line will appear as a point. The desired line perpendicular to the plane will be the common perpendicular, and since it appears in its point view when the plane appears true size, the common perpendicular will be where the two skew lines cross.

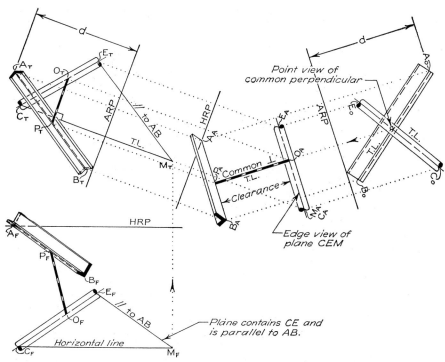

FIG. 97. Common perpendicular to two skew lines (line-and-plane method).

Figure 97 shows the construction of the plane CEM which contains one of the two skew lines and is parallel to the other. The plane CEM appears in its edge view in the auxiliary view projected off the top view, and the common perpendicular will appear in its true length, but its position cannot yet be located. The point view of the common perpendicular is located in the secondary auxiliary view where the skew lines AB and CE cross. The direction of the top view of the common perpendicular must be perpendicular to the line of sight for the auxiliary view projected off the top view because the common perpendicular is true length in this auxiliary view. Graphical inaccuracies of projection must *not* be permitted to alter this direction. See Art. 47 for the two-line-method solution to this problem.

74. COMMON PERPENDICULAR TO TWO SKEW LINES (Two-plane Method)

Figure 98 shows pictorially the construction of the plane $ABSR$ perpendicular to the plane which contains the skew line CE and is parallel to the skew line AB. The plane $ABSR$ is formed by the two lines AR and BS drawn perpendicularly to plane CEM. Points S and R are the piercing points of the two perpendiculars through points A and B with the plane CEM. One end of the common perpendicular is located at the intersection point O of the line of intersection SR of the two planes with line CE. The common perpendicular is the line drawn through point O and parallel to AR and BS.

In Fig. 99 the plane which contains skew line CE and is parallel to skew line AB is CEM. Its edge view is shown in the auxiliary view. The perpendicular lines through A and B are true length in the auxiliary view and are perpendicular to the plane CEM. The piercing points are S and R. Since AR and BS are true length in the auxiliary view, the direction of their top views is automatically determined. RS, as it intersects CE in the top view, locates the point O end of the common perpendicular. OP will be parallel to AR and BS.

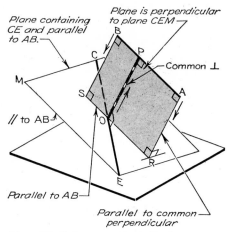

Fig. 98. Common perpendicular to two skew lines (two-plane method).

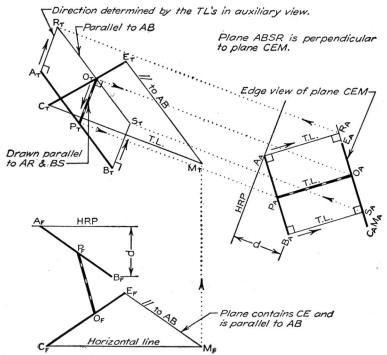

Fig. 99. Common perpendicular to two skew lines (two-plane method).

75. THE SHORTEST HORIZONTAL LINE CONNECTING TWO SKEW LINES

The shortest horizontal line connecting two skew lines will be *true length* when the plane which contains one skew line and is parallel to the other appears in its edge view. All *other* horizontal lines connecting these two skew lines will appear *foreshortened* in this view, thus making them *longer in space*. In Fig. 100 the edge view of the plane *ABM* which contains *AB* and is parallel to *CE* is in the auxiliary view projected off the top view. Since $C_A E_A$ is parallel to the edge view of the plane, all horizontal lines (parallel to *HRP*) will appear to be of equal length. However, only one will be true length in this view. Thus, it will be the shortest horizontal connecting line. Its elevation will be determined in another auxiliary view whose line of sight will be parallel to the true-length connecting line. Its point view will be where lines *AB* and *CE* cross in that view. Even though the shortest horizontal line is also true length in the top view, its direction in the top view must be perpendicular to the line of sight for the auxiliary view. The surface formed by *all* horizontal lines connecting two skew lines is a hyperbolic paraboloid (see Art. 177 and the auxiliary view of Fig. 241*a*).

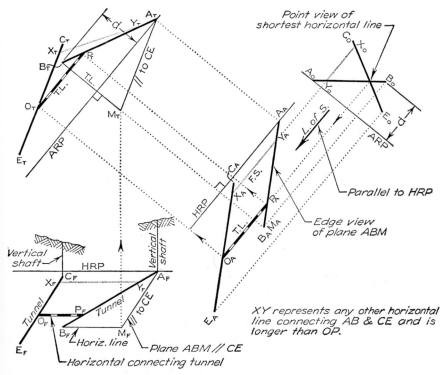

Fig. 100. Shortest horizontal line connecting two skew lines.

76. THE SHORTEST LINE AT A SPECIFIED SLOPE CONNECTING TWO SKEW LINES

The shortest line at a specified slope (see Fig. 101) connecting two skew lines will be *true length* when the plane which contains one skew line and is parallel to the other appears in its edge view.   All *other* lines at this slope connecting the same skew lines will appear *foreshortened* in this view, thereby making them *longer in space*.   The two skew lines of Fig. 101 represent center lines of two pipes at 25% grade (slope) on the side of a mountain.   They are to be connected by the shortest line at the same slope or grade.   Plane *ABM* contains skew line *AB* and is parallel to skew line *CE*.   The edge view of plane *ABM* appears in an auxiliary view projected off the top view where slope and grade may be measured (see Art. 81).   All lines at this slope connecting the two skew lines will appear to be of equal length in this view.   However, there will be only one line true length, and with all the others foreshortened, the true-length line will be the shortest.   Another view with its line of sight taken parallel

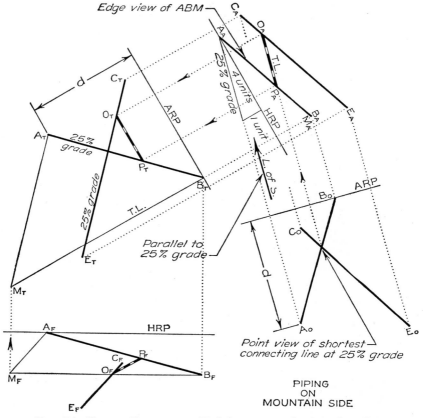

Fig. 101. Shortest line at a specified slope connecting two skew lines.

to the true-length line will have its point view of the line located where lines AB and CE cross. The top view of the desired line must be perpendicular to the line of sight for the primary auxiliary view. See Art. 110 for another line connecting two skew lines.

77. THE ANGLE A LINE MAKES WITH THE HRP (Auxiliary-view Method)

The angle a line makes with the horizontal reference plane (or any other plane) is the angle between the line and its perpendicular projection onto the plane. In Fig. 102a point B is on the HRP while A has been projected to it by the perpendicular projector AA_T, with A_T as the piercing point and BA_T as the projected line. In order to measure the angle which will be designated Θ_H, the line of sight for the view must be perpendicular to the plane of the *triangle* BA_TA which is perpendicular to HRP.

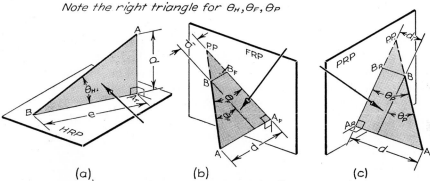

The plane of the shaded right triangle which is perpendicular to the reference plane must be viewed true size in order to have the true angle of the line with the reference plane show.

FIG. 102. The angle a line makes with the reference planes.

In Fig. 103 the plane of the *triangle* appears in its edge view in the top view coincident with line A_TB_T. A true size view of this triangle gives the true value of Θ_H. The five components of the right triangle must all be true size in this view with the exception of the reference plane which must be in its edge view. They are explained in Art. 78.

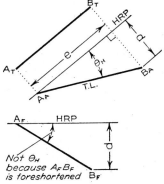

FIG. 103. The angle a line makes with HRP.

78. THE FIVE BASIC COMPONENTS OF AN AUXILIARY VIEW SHOWING THE TRUE ANGLE A LINE MAKES WITH A REFERENCE PLANE

The five basic components are shown in Fig. 104 and explained as follows:

1. The dimension e is the projection of the line onto the desired reference plane as shown in Figs. 102a and 103.

2. The reference plane must appear in its edge view when the triangle is found true size, since the plane of the triangle is perpendicular to the desired reference plane.

3. The perpendicular distance of each end of the line from the desired reference plane *must be maintained*. If either distance is changed, the angle will likewise change.

4. The true length of the line is required. If the line is not true length, the apparent angle will be *greater* than the true angle. The front view of the triangle in Fig. 103 is not so wide as the true triangle of the auxiliary view.

5. The angle the line makes with the desired reference plane must be true size in this view. If this angle were given and some of the others of the above four items were not known, they could be obtained by constructing the auxiliary view from the known items. The true Θ_H could not be used directly to construct the front view of Fig. 103.

The combined angles Θ_H, Θ_F, and Θ_P do *not* ordinarily add up to 90°. Those of Figs. 103, 105, and 106 of the *same* line add up to 105°.

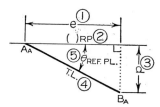

Fig. 104. The five basic elements of an auxiliary view, giving the angle a line makes with a plane.

79. THE ANGLE A LINE MAKES WITH THE FRP
(Auxiliary-view Method)

The plane of the triangle containing the true Θ_F of Fig. 102b is perpendicular to FRP, appears in its edge view in the front view, and contains A_FB_F. The auxiliary view of Fig. 105 whose line of sight is perpendicular to A_FB_F includes all of the five basic items for the Θ_F angle.

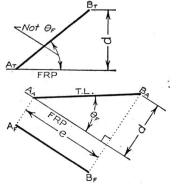

Fig. 105. The angle a line makes with FRP.

80. THE ANGLE A LINE MAKES WITH PRP (Auxiliary-view Method)

The plane of the triangle containing the true Θ_P of Fig. 102c is perpendicular to PRP. Thus the Θ_P will be found in an auxiliary view projected off the side view. The plane of the triangle will appear in its edge view in the side view of Fig. 106 and will contain A_RB_R. The auxiliary view showing the triangle true size will contain all five of the basic components of the Θ_P triangle.

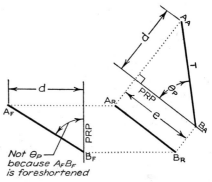

Not Θ_P because A_FB_F is foreshortened

FIG. 106. The angle a line makes with PRP.

81. PRACTICAL METHODS OF INDICATING SLOPE OF A PLANE

The slope of a line or plane in practice is the angle Θ_H, although it is seldom expressed as such. Figure 107 lists several industrial names given to this angle. They *all* require the edge view of HRP. In other words, they cannot be measured in auxiliary views projected off the front or side views.

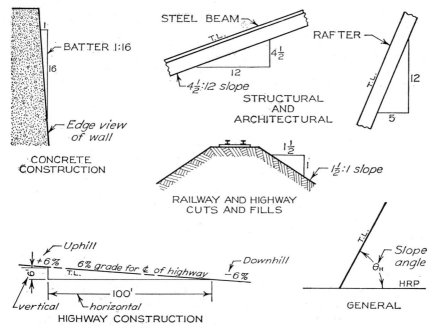

FIG. 107. Practical methods of indicating slope of a line or plane.

82. TO CONSTRUCT A LINE AT A SPECIFIED SLOPE (or Grade)

The data for the construction of a line at a specified slope are given in Fig. 108a. Since the slope of a line is Θ_H merely expressed in industrial terms, the true size of the Θ_H triangle will be in an auxiliary view projected off the top view. The 5 to 12 ratio will be measured as indicated for a steel beam but reversed for a rafter (see Fig. 107). The true length of the line is measured *after* the amount of slope has been made. Point B_A of Fig. 108b may now be projected to the top view and thence to the front view as shown in Fig. 108c. See note on Fig. 108 as to how grade would have been measured. Grade is the natural tangent of Θ_H of the line multiplied by 100.

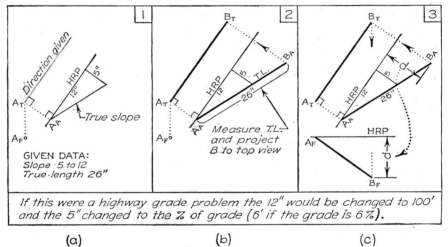

If this were a highway grade problem the 12" would be changed to 100' and the 5" changed to the % of grade (6' if the grade is 6%).

(a)   (b)   (c)

Fig. 108. Constructing a line at a specified slope.

83. THE ANGLE A LINE MAKES WITH AN INCLINED OR OBLIQUE PLANE (Auxiliary-view Method)

Whether the plane is a reference plane, inclined plane, or oblique plane, the fundamentals involved in obtaining the angle between the line and the plane are the *same*. The inclined or oblique plane must be found *true size* as was necessary when the plane involved was a reference plane. When Θ_F was required, the *FRP* was found true size in the front view and an auxiliary view was projected off that view which would show Θ_F (see Fig. 102b).

The angle a line makes with an inclined plane will require two auxiliary views, one to find the plane true size and the other to find the line true length in the *same* view in which the plane again appears as an edge.

The angle a line makes with an oblique plane is illustrated in Fig. 109.

Plane 1-2-3-4 is first found in its edge view, then true size as were the cases of the inclined plane and the reference planes. In the third auxiliary view, the plane 1-2-3-4 again appears in its edge view and in addition line AB appears true length. A_oB_o is dimension e of Fig. 104. See Fig. 95 for a pictorial of the angle between a line and an oblique plane.

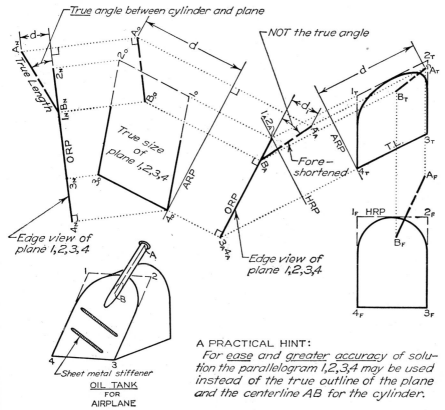

A PRACTICAL HINT:
For *ease* and *greater* *accuracy* of solution the parallelogram 1,2,3,4 may be used instead of the true outline of the plane and the centerline AB for the cylinder.

Fig. 109. The angle between a line and an oblique plane (auxiliary-view method).

84. THE ANGLE BETWEEN A LINE AND ANY PLANE (Point-view-of-line Method)

The angle between a line and *any* plane may be found by first finding the point view of the line and then taking the next auxiliary view in such a direction that the plane will appear in its edge view. The line will automatically be true length in that view because, when a line appears as a point in one view, any view projected from that view will have its line of sight perpendicular to the line.

In Fig. 110 line 1-2 appears true length in the auxiliary view projected from the front view and as a point in the secondary auxiliary view. With line B_AE_A added to the primary auxiliary view perpendicular to the line

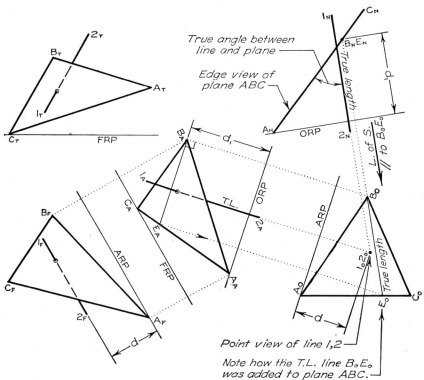

FIG. 110. The angle between a line and an oblique plane (point-view-of-line method).

of sight for the secondary auxiliary view, line B_oE_o will be true length in the secondary auxiliary view. The line of sight for the third auxiliary view is taken parallel to the true-length line B_oE_o. The plane ABC will, therefore, appear in its edge view, and the line 1-2 true length in the third auxiliary view. The angle between the line and plane is indicated on the drawing.

Figure 111 shows additional applications of the angle between a line and a plane.

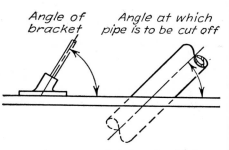

FIG .111. Applications of angle between a line (∠) and a plane.

85. REPRESENTING A PLANE AT A SPECIFIED ANGLE TO A REFERENCE PLANE

Figure 112 shows three solutions to a problem requiring the construction of a plane which slopes upward toward the rear with $\Theta_F = 45°$ and a frontal line of the plane given. *All* points higher in the front view than the given frontal line AB are in the rear of the FRP containing AB. With the edge view of the plane drawn through the point view of the frontal line AB at 45° to FRP, point E_A of Fig. 112a may be chosen at random along the edge view of the plane. Point E_A when projected to the front view will be above the given frontal line. The auxiliary view shows E_A to be to the rear of FRP and the front view above the frontal line; thus, the plane slopes upward and to the rear. E_F may be located in the front view *any place* along its projection line from the auxiliary view, but once the front view of E has been chosen, its top view will be directly above the front view of the point.

In Fig. 112b points M_F and N_F in the front view may be chosen *anywhere* along the projection line from the auxiliary view where the point view of this line was first chosen. Project to the top view as indicated.

In Fig. 112c it has been shown that points to be chosen on the edge view of the plane need not be limited to one side of the frontal line.

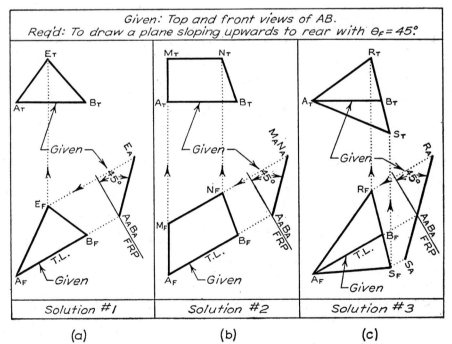

FIG. 112. Representing a plane at a specified angle to a reference plane.

For additional methods of representing planes at specified angles to reference planes, see Arts. 109 and 134.

86. LINE OF INTERSECTION OF TWO PLANES (Auxiliary-view Method)

The line of intersection of two planes may be determined by drawing the edge view of *either* of the two planes and finding where at least two lines of one plane pierce the edge view of the other plane. In Fig. 113 the plane ABC appears in its edge view in the auxiliary view. Line MN pierces this plane at piercing point $PP^\#1$, and line MO pierces the plane at piercing point $PP^\#2$. In connecting the front view of the two piercing points $PP^\#1$ and $PP^\#2$, it becomes obvious that plane ABC actually includes $PP^\#2$ only when it is extended. Line BC of plane ABC pierces plane MNO

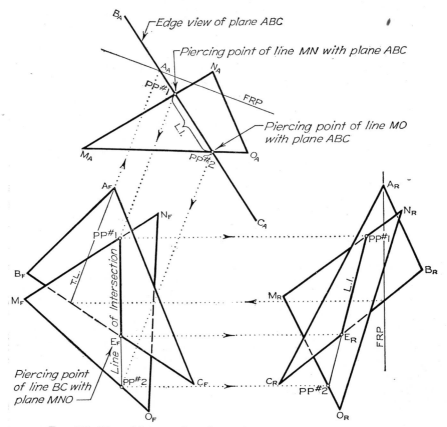

Fig. 113. Line of intersection of two planes (auxiliary-view method).

at point E where $B_F C_F$ intersects the line of intersection. $PP^{\#}1\,E$ becomes the useful part of the line of intersection. $PP^{\#}2$ corresponds to points M and N of Fig. 114.

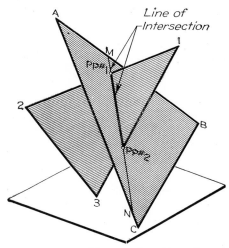

FIG. 114. Line of intersection of two planes.

87. LINE OF INTERSECTION OF TWO PLANES (by Cutting-plane Method of Finding the Piercing Point of a Line with a Plane)

All lines of *either* plane of two intersecting planes pierce the other plane except those lines which are parallel to the line of intersection of the two planes (see Fig. 114). Points on the line of intersection may be determined by finding where individual lines of *either* plane pierce the other plane as explained in Art. 71 and shown pictorially in Fig. 91.

In Fig. 115a lines $3_T 4_T$ and $5_T 4_T$ were assumed to be edge views of two planes perpendicular to HRP. The intersections of these two cutting planes with plane $ABCD$ are $M_F O_F$ and $N_F R_F$, respectively. Line 3-4 pierces plane $ABCD$ where $3_F 4_F$ intersects $M_F O_F$. Line 5-4 pierces plane $ABCD$ where $5_F 4_F$ intersects $N_F R_F$.

In Fig. 115b no line of either plane in either view crosses two given lines of the other plane. In order to solve the problem using this method, it is necessary to *extend* some of the lines until they *cross* two lines of the other plane. Line $M_F P_F$ is extended until it crosses $A_F C_F$ at 5_F. Line $M_F P_F 5_F$ is assumed to be the edge view of a cutting plane perpendicular to FRP. The line of intersection of this cutting plane with plane ABC is 4-5. Piercing point $PP^{\#}2$ is found where $4_T 5_T$ intersects $M_T P_T$. Since *all* lines

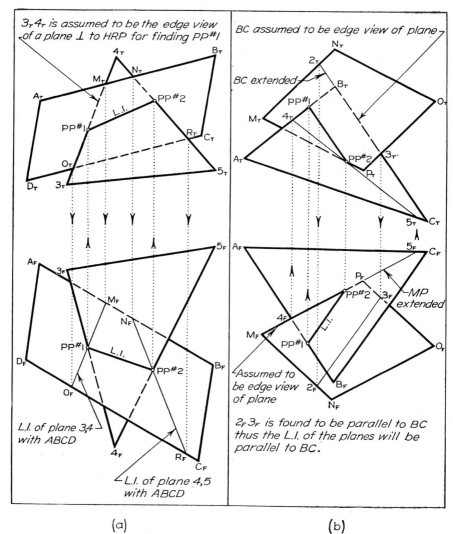

FIG. 115. Line of intersection of two planes.

of either plane pierce the other plane except those which are parallel to the line of intersection of the two planes, it is *not* necessary to find where another line of plane $MNOP$ pierces plane ABC in order to find the line of intersection of the two planes.

Line BC of plane ABC is chosen for the location of a second piercing point on the line of intersection of the two planes. $B_T C_T$ is extended to 2_T, and the line is assumed to be the edge view of a cutting plane perpendicular to HRP. The line of intersection of this cutting plane with plane $MNOP$ is 2_F3_F, but it is found to be parallel to line B_FC_F rather than to intersect it.   This is an application of Fig. 93c.   Line BC of plane ABC has now been proved to be parallel to plane $MNOP$; therefore it is *parallel* to the line of intersection of the two planes.   Piercing point $PP^\#1$ may now be located by drawing the line of intersection through $PP^\#2$ and parallel to BC.   As a check on graphical accuracy and possible errors of projection, three points on the line of intersection of the two planes should be determined.   If the three points do not form a straight line, an error in accuracy or projection exists.

88. LINE OF INTERSECTION OF TWO PLANES (Random Cutting-plane Method)

A cutting plane taken at *random* will intersect two intersecting planes in two lines of intersection whose point of intersection will be one point on the line of intersection of the two original planes.   The edge view of a normal cutting plane of Fig. 116 is such a plane.   This cutting plane intersects plane ABC along line 10-11 and plane 5-6-7-8 along line 12-13.

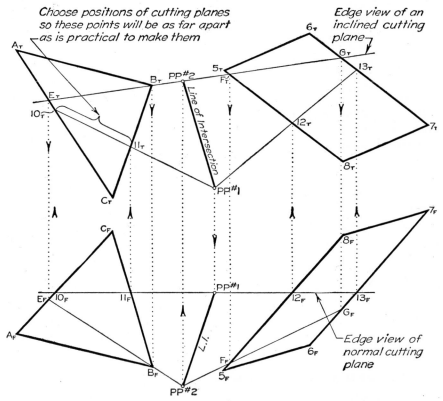

FIG. 116. Line of intersection of two planes (cutting-plane method).

The extension of these two cutting plane lines of intersection 10-11 and
12-13 intersect at piercing point $PP^{\#}1$ which is one point along the line of
intersection of the two planes ABC and 5-6-7-8.   The front view of $PP^{\#}1$
will be on the edge view of the cutting plane.   Planes ABC, 5-6-7-8 and
the normal cutting plane form a pyramid in space.   The piercing point
$PP^{\#}1$ is the vertex of this pyramid, lines of intersection 10-11 and 12-13
are two of the three edges of this pyramid, and the line of intersection of
the two planes ABC and 5-6-7-8 which is yet to be found is the third edge.

The edge view of the cutting planes need not be restricted to the front
view, nor need the planes be normal planes.   The second cutting plane
appears in its edge view in the top view and is an inclined plane.   This
cutting plane intersects plane ABC along line EB and plane 5-6-7-8 along
line FG.   The front view of these two cutting-plane lines of intersection,
$E_F B_F$ and $F_F G_F$, intersect to give piercing point $PP^{\#}2$, which, when projected to the top view, will be on the edge view of the cutting plane.

89. THE ANGLE BETWEEN A PLANE AND HRP

The angle between a plane and the horizontal reference plane is the
angle between the edge views of both planes.   In Fig. 117 it may be seen
that, in order to find the edge view of both planes in one view, it is necessary to have the line of sight for the view parallel to the line of intersection
of the two planes.   The line of
intersection of a horizontal plane
with *any* plane will be a horizontal
line.   In the point view of this
horizontal line of intersection,
each of the two planes, HRP and
the other plane, will appear in its
edge view and each will contain
the point view of the line of intersections.   This view is actually
the true size of the right section
illustrated in Fig. 117.

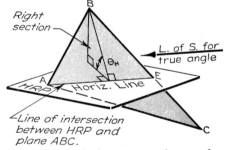

FIG. 117. Angle between a plane and a
reference plane.

In Fig. 118, $A_T E_T$ is the true length of the line of intersection of plane
ABC with HRP.   The auxiliary view projected from the top view contains the point view of AE and the edge view of each of the two planes.
As a precaution against inaccuracy or error in projection, project more
than one point of plane ABC in addition to the horizontal line of intersection AE to the auxiliary view.

90. THE ANGLE BETWEEN A PLANE AND FRP

The angle between a plane and the frontal reference plane is obtained
in a view where the frontal line of intersection of the two planes appears

in its point view and the planes appear in their edge views. In Fig. 118 frontal line AK is the line of intersection of FRP with plane ABC. Since AK is true length in the front view, an auxiliary view projected from the front view with its line of sight parallel to A_FK_F will contain the point view of AK and the edge view of each plane.

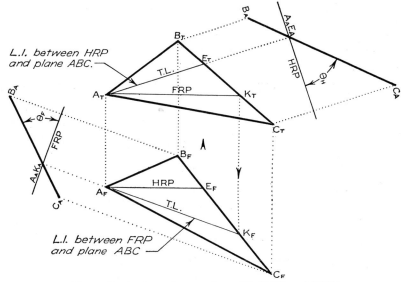

FIG. 118. Angle a plane makes with HRP and FRP.

91. THE ANGLE BETWEEN A PLANE AND *PRP*

The angle between a plane and the profile reference plane will appear in a view where the profile line of intersection of the two planes appears in its point view and the planes in their edge views. In Fig. 119 the profile line of intersection is BE. Since B_RE_R is true length in the side view, an auxiliary view whose line of sight is parallel to B_RE_R will contain the point of view of this line of intersection and the edge view of each plane.

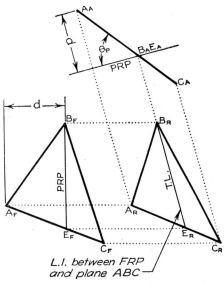

FIG. 119. Angle a plane makes with PRP.

92. THE ANGLE BETWEEN ANY TWO PLANES (Edge-view-of-planes Method)

The angle between any two planes may be obtained in the point view of the line of intersection of the two planes. In the left side portion of Fig. 120, A_TF_T is the top view of the line of intersection of planes $AFGB$ and $AFJE$. An intermediary view is necessary in order to obtain the true length of the line of intersection. From this auxiliary view is projected the secondary auxiliary view which contains the point view of the line of intersection A_oF_o and the edge view of each plane. Note that more than one point of each plane in addition to the line of intersection AF was projected into the secondary auxiliary view. The angle between the planes is the angle between the edge views of the planes.

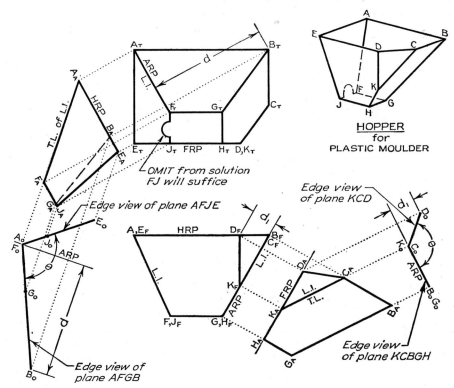

Fig. 120. Angle between two planes.

The true angle between any two intersecting planes is actually the right section of the two planes. This is illustrated in Fig. 121, where the right section is shown perpendicular to the line of intersection and intersects both planes at AC and AE. The angle between the planes is CAE and is obtained in the view where the line of sight is parallel to the line of intersection of the two planes. Several applications of angles between planes are shown in Fig. 122. In Arts. 93, 94, and 117 will be found additional methods of obtaining the angle between planes.

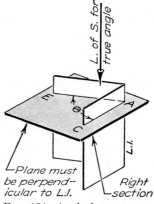

Fig. 121. Angle between two planes (right-section method).

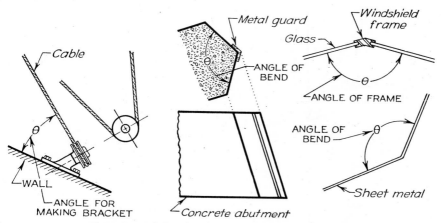

Fig. 122. Applications of angle between two planes.

93. THE ANGLE BETWEEN ANY TWO PLANES WITHOUT USE OF THE LINE OF INTERSECTION

The use of the line of intersection in finding the angle between any two planes may be avoided by finding one plane true size and then the other plane in its edge view in a view projected from the true-size view of the first plane.

In Fig. 123 plane 1-2-3-4 appears in its edge view in the auxiliary view
projected off the top view and true size in the secondary auxiliary view.
In *any* view projected off the secondary auxiliary view, the plane 1-2-3-4
will again appear in its edge view and perpendicular to the line of sight
for that view.   Thus, plane 1-2-3-4 automatically appears in its edge
view in the third auxiliary view.   By adding the true-length line A_oE_o
to the plane ABC (which represents the plane of the cable and pulley) in
the secondary auxiliary view, the direction of the third auxiliary view is
obtained where plane ABC will appear in its edge view as does plane
1-2-3-4.   The line of sight for the third auxiliary view is parallel to the
true length of A_oE_o of plane ABC.

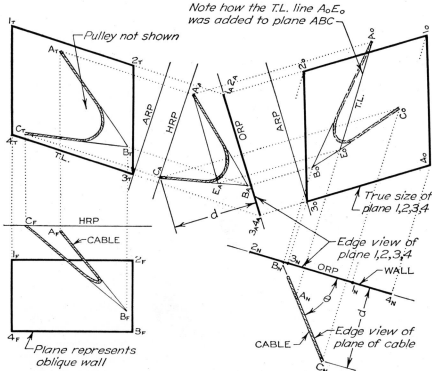

FIG. 123. Angle between two planes without use of line of intersection.

94. THE ANGLE BETWEEN ANY TWO PLANES (Lines-perpendicular-to-planes Method)

The angle between two planes may be measured by two lines drawn
through *any* point perpendicularly to the two planes.   In Fig. 124 point
O is chosen at random, line OE drawn perpendicularly to plane 1, and

line OK drawn perpendicularly to plane 2. plane OKE, the angle α may be measured. is $180° - \alpha$.

In Fig. 125 point O was chosen at a convenient place. Two lines have been drawn through point O with one line perpendicular to plane ABC and the other line perpendicular to plane 1-2-3. Note the use of horizontal and frontal lines to obtain the perpendicular lines. The horizontal line RS has been added to the plane of the perpendicular lines in order that the edge and true-size views of this plane could be obtained. The first auxiliary view gives the edge view of the plane ROS, and the secondary auxiliary view the true size of the plane and angles α and θ.

By finding the true size of the The angle between the planes

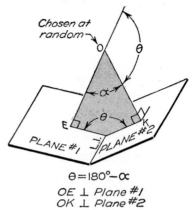

$\theta = 180° - \alpha$
$OE \perp$ Plane #1
$OK \perp$ Plane #2

FIG. 124. Angle between two planes (perpendicular-lines method).

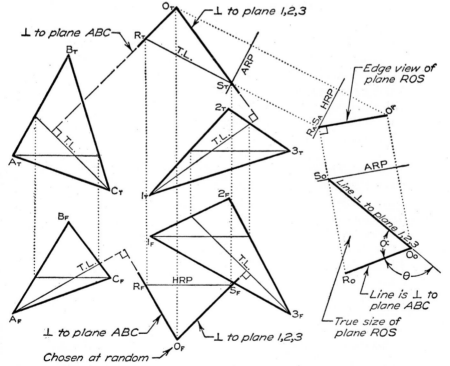

FIG. 125. Angle between two planes (perpendicular-lines method).

CHAPTER 7

REVOLUTION

95. THE PURPOSE OF THE REVOLUTION METHOD

Revolution is the revolving of points, lines, and planes about lines instead of taking auxiliary views or at least a lesser number of them in order to obtain the solution to certain problems. To illustrate, revolution eliminates taking an auxiliary view in order to obtain the true length of a line and the angle it makes with a reference plane.

96. BASIC ELEMENTS OF REVOLUTION

All revolution is based on revolving points about lines. Lines and planes are revolved about a line by revolving the points of the ends of the line and corners of the plane about the given line as the axis of revolution.

The basic elements of revolution are:

1. A point revolves about a line (axis) in the path of a *circle* (see Fig. 126) with the center of the circle on the line.

2. The path of the circle of revolution appears as a circle when the line (axis) appears in its point view (see Fig. 127).

3. When the line (axis) appears in its true length, the path of revolution appears as a straight line equal in length to the diameter of the circle and perpendicular to the line (axis) (see Fig. 127).

4. When the line (axis) is foreshortened, the path of revolution will *always* appear as an *ellipse* with the major axis of the ellipse equal in length to the diameter of the circle (see Fig. 128).

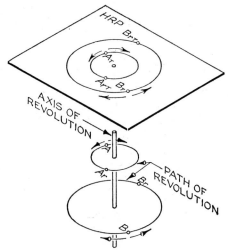

Fig. 126. Revolving a point about a line.

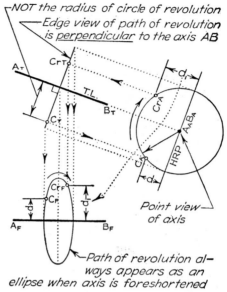

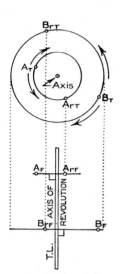

Fig. 127. Revolving
a point about a line.

Fig. 128. Revolving a point about a line.

97. REVOLVING A POINT ABOUT A LINE (Axis)

A point may be revolved either clockwise or counterclockwise about
the axis. *Only* the point view of the axis determines the radius of the
circle of revolution (see Figs. 126 and 127). The revolved positions are
designated by a lower-case subscript (r). Note that A_F and A_{rF} of Fig.
127 are both on the edge view of the circle which is perpendicular to the
axis.

In Fig. 128 the axis is TL in the top view and appears in its point view
in the auxiliary view. The distance of C_A from the point view of the axis
determines the radius of the circle of revolution.

A series of positions of C_{rA} first taken in the auxiliary view on the circle
of revolution, then projected to the top view of the path of revolution, and
then projected to the front view as C_{rF} was located would establish the
ellipse view of the path of revolution. A d_1 measurement must be taken
from the auxiliary view to the front view for each position of C_{rA}.

98. EXTREME POSITIONS ON THE PATH OF REVOLUTION

The extreme positions on the path of revolution are readily established
from the *straight-line view* of the path of revolution. Figure 129 should
be compared with Fig. 39. The highest and lowest positions are established in an auxiliary view projected off the top view, the closest to the

front and farthest to the rear in an auxiliary view projected off the front view, and farthest to left or right in an auxiliary view projected off the side view.

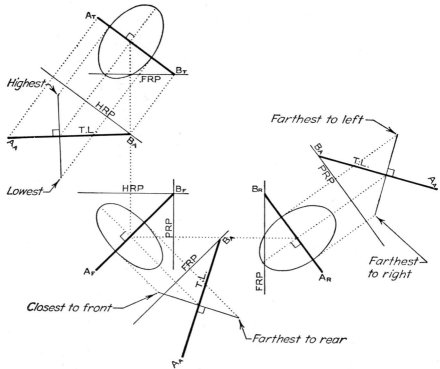

Major axis of ellipse is __always__ equal to diameter of circle of revolution and perpendicular to axis of revolution

FIG. 129. Extreme positions on the path of revolution.

When it is necessary to establish an extreme position of a point on the path of revolution in a view where the path appears as an ellipse, the point is located where the reference plane touches the path of revolution, as C_R in Fig. 130. Since the major axis of the ellipse is equal to the diameter of the circle, the ellipse may be revolved about its major axis until it appears as the true-size view of the path of revolution which is a circle. The point C_R is located by drawing a line through E_R where the extended major axis of the ellipse pierces the FRP. The line $E_R C_{rR}$ is drawn tangent to the circle. C_{rR} is the revolved position of C_R which,

when revolved about the major axis
back to *FRP* and the ellipse, locates
the farthest forward point on the path of
revolution. See Art. 144 for further
information on lines tangent to ellipses.

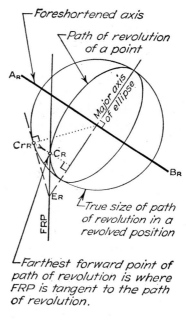

FIG. 130. Locating the farthest forward point on
the ellipse view of the path of revolution.

99. REVOLVING A LINE ABOUT ANOTHER LINE

The four geometric shapes generated by a line revolving about another
line as an axis are illustrated in Fig. 131.   The cone is the most commonly
used geometric shape in revolution problems.

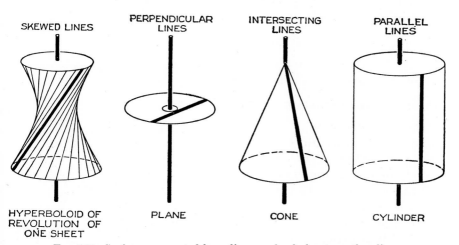

FIG. 131. Surfaces generated by a line revolved about another line.

In Fig. 132 *assume* the base plane to be *HRP*. Line *AB* makes θ° with *HRP*. The right triangle as explained in Art. 77 is represented by a celluloid drafting triangle in Fig. 132. By revolving the triangle about the side of the right triangle which is perpendicular to *HRP* and contains point *A*, the line *AB* generates a cone whose base is in *HRP*. When the right triangle is viewed true size, the θ_H and true length of *AB* in their revolved position may be measured.

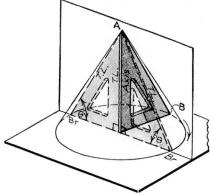

Fɪɢ. 132. Revolving a line to find its angle with a plane.

100. BASIC ELEMENTS OF THE CONE OF REVOLUTION AS USED IN FINDING THE ANGLE A LINE MAKES WITH ANY PLANE

These basic elements are:

1. The base of the right circular cone must lie in or parallel to the plane.
2. The axis of the cone must be perpendicular to the plane.
3. The line must be an element of the cone.
4. The radius of the base of the cone is the length of the projection of the line onto the plane (dimension *e* of Fig. 102a).
5. The two views of the plane necessary to solve for this angle are the edge and true-size views.
6. The two views of the cone necessary to solve for this angle are the point and true-length views of the axis of the cone.

101. THE ANGLE A LINE MAKES WITH *HRP*

The generated cone of Fig. 131, which will give the true length of the line and the angle it makes with *HRP*, will have *either* end of the line as the vertex of the cone and the other end of the line on the circular base of the cone. The axis of the cone will be perpendicular to *HRP*, and the base will lie in a *HRP* as shown in Fig. 133. $A_T B_T$ is the *e* measurement of Figs. 102a and 103 which determines the radius of the base of the cone to be drawn in the true

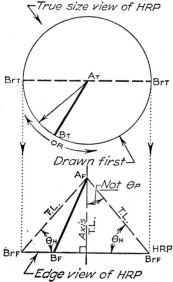

Fɪɢ. 133. Finding the angle a line makes with HRP.

size view of *HRP*. The size of the base is projected to the front view where *HRP* appears in its edge view. With the vertex of the cone at A_F and the base containing *HRP* and B_F, the front view of the cone may be drawn in its isosceles triangle view. *Both* contour elements A_FB_{rF} give the true length of the line *AB* and the angle the line makes with *HRP*. Note that B_T has been revolved to B_{rT} in the top view, which will make A_FB_{rF} true length in the front view.

102. THE ANGLE A LINE MAKES WITH *FRP*

A generated cone similar to the cone in Fig. 131 having its base in an *FRP* with one end of the given line on the base of the cone and the other end as its vertex will give the true length and Θ_F of the line. The cone will appear in its circular view in the front view. The front view of the line will be the radius of the base of the cone. The top view of the cone will be an isosceles triangle with the axis of the cone true length and perpendicular to *FRP*. The contour elements of the cone will be true length, and their angle with the base of the cone will be Θ_F for the line (see Fig. 135 for Θ_F cone).

103. THE ANGLE A LINE MAKES WITH *PRP*

The base of the generated cone must lie in a *PRP*, the axis of the cone perpendicular to *PRP* and the line (see *AB* of Fig. 134) an element of the cone. The side view of the line will be the radius of the base of the cone. The contour elements of the front view of the cone will be true length, and the angle they make with the base of the cone will be Θ_P.

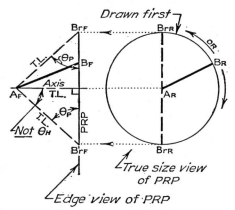

FIG. 134. Finding the angle a line makes with PRP.

104. ONE GENERATED CONE GIVES ONLY ONE $\Theta_{\text{REF PLANE}}$

The top view of Fig. 135 shows the isosceles triangle view of the Θ_F and Θ_P cones of the line AB. The Θ_F cone will *not* also give the angle Θ_P. The Θ_P cone as shown has less height than the Θ_F cone. The distance of the two points (height of the cone) relative to the plane with which the angle is desired *must not* be changed. B_{rT} on the Θ_F cone is farther away than B_T from the PRP containing A_T, thereby changing the angle of the line with PRP.

105. THE ANGLE A LINE MAKES WITH AN INCLINED PLANE

The angle a line makes with an inclined plane is obtained in the *same* views of the plane needed to find Θ_H, Θ_F, or Θ_P; that is, *the edge view and the true-size view of the plane are required.* In Fig. 136 plane 1-2-3 appears in its edge view in the front view and true size in the auxiliary view projected off the front view. The radius of the base of the cone will be the length of the line as it appears in the true-size view of the plane. The axis of the cone will be true length and perpendicular to the edge view of the plane in the front view. *Either* end of the line may be the vertex of the cone, and the base will contain the other end of the line and be perpendicular to the axis of the cone as well as parallel to the edge view of the plane, since neither end of the line lies in

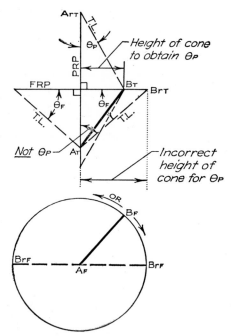

FIG. 135. Proof that only one Θ can be obtained with one cone or revolution.

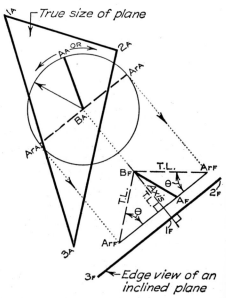

FIG. 136. Finding the angle a line makes with an inclined plane.

the plane 1-2-3. The contour elements of the cone will be true length, and the angle they make with their base will be the angle the line AB makes with plane 1-2-3.

106. THE ANGLE A LINE MAKES WITH AN OBLIQUE PLANE

The edge view and the true-size view of the plane are necessary in order to determine the angle a line makes with an oblique plane. The plane 1-2-3-4 of Fig. 137 appears in its edge view in an auxiliary view projected off the front view. The axis of the cone will be true length and perpendicular to the edge view of the plane. One end of the line is the vertex, and the other end is on the edge view of the cone's base which will be parallel to the edge view of the plane.

The true-size view of the plane will also show the circular view of the cone. The length of the line A_oB_o as it appears in the secondary auxiliary view will be the radius of the cone's base. The contour elements of the cone in the edge view of the plane will be true length, and their angle with the base of the cone will be the angle the line makes with the plane 1-2-3-4.

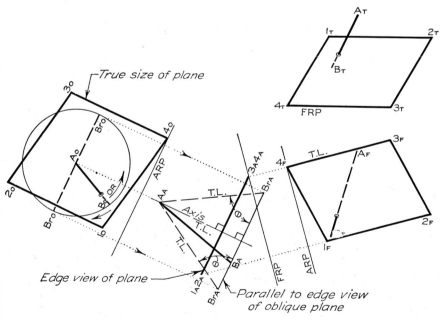

FIG. 137. Finding the angle a line makes with an oblique plane.

107. A LINE MAKING SPECIFIED ANGLES WITH TWO REFERENCE PLANES

A line making a 30° angle with *FRP* and a 45° angle with *HRP* is explained in Fig. 138. *Any* line containing point *A* and making 30° with *FRP* will lie on a Θ_F cone whose base lies in a *FRP* and whose elements make 30° with *FRP*. Any line containing point *A* and making 45° with *HRP* will lie on a Θ_H cone whose base lies in a *HRP* and whose elements make 45° with *HRP*. By having the vertices of the two cones at the common point *A*, the line of intersection of the two cones will be two straight lines through point *A* as shown in the pictorial. Since the two lines of intersection *AB* and *AE* (Fig. 138) of the two cones lie on both cones, the two lines make 30° with *FRP* and 45° with *HRP*. If the base of the frontal cone had been placed in front of *A* as indicated by the dotted lines, the lines of intersection would have been *AC* and *AD*. Thus there are four possible solutions. The requirements of the problem would have to specify which solution is needed.

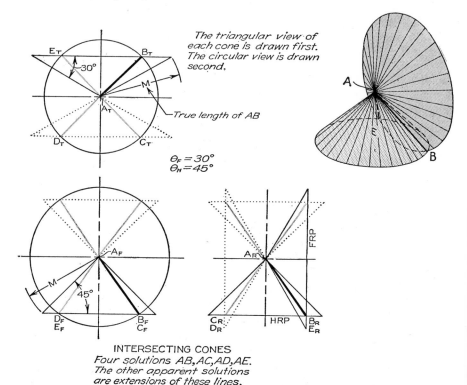

The triangular view of each cone is drawn first. The circular view is drawn second.

True length of AB

$\Theta_F = 30°$
$\Theta_H = 45°$

INTERSECTING CONES
Four solutions AB, AC, AD, AE.
The other apparent solutions
are extensions of these lines.

FIG. 138. A line making specified angles with two reference planes.

Since one end of each solution is to be at point A which will be the vertex of each cone, the other end must be on the base of each cone. This necessitates that the elements of *all* cones must be of the *same* length. Note that in Fig. 138 all elements of the several cones are of length M. The other end of each solution, whether it be B, C, D, or E, is where the bases of the two cones on which it lies intersect. Note that the point B is on the base of *both* cones in *every* view.

Figure 139 shows the four solutions and that the other apparent solutions are merely extensions of the four solutions.

The given angles a line makes with two reference planes must total 90° or less. This is illustrated in Fig. 140.

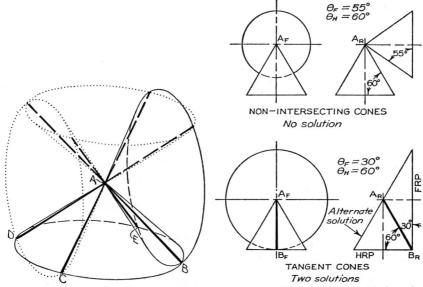

Fig. 139. Pictorial of the four lines making specified angles with two reference planes.

Fig. 140. A line making specified angles with two reference planes.

An application of a line at specified angles to two reference planes is shown in Fig. 141. The two reference planes are HRP and PRP. The notes and steps make the illustration self-explanatory. After the line AB has been located, a table of constants, K and K_1, may be made for various perpendicular distances d between the two pipes at right angles to each other.

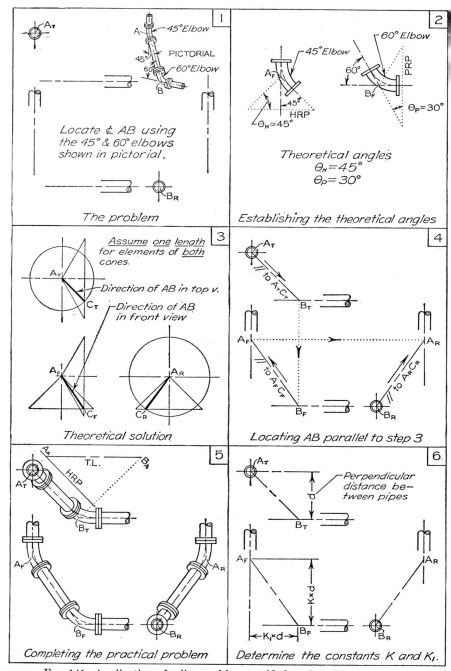

Fig. 141. Application of a line making specified angles with two planes.

108. A LINE MAKING SPECIFIED ANGLES WITH ANY TWO PLANES

Let planes 1 and 2 of Fig. 142 represent *any* two planes. Find the edge views of *both* planes in the same view. Through point *A* construct the triangular views of both cones with axes perpendicular to their respective planes. The elements of both cones *must* be of the *same* length. One view of point *B* is obtained where the edge views of the two bases intersect. The circular view of either base will locate point *B* in a second view as indicated in Fig. 142. With two views of the line thus obtained, any other desired views may be drawn.

109. CONSTRUCT A PLANE AT SPECIFIED ANGLES TO TWO REFERENCE PLANES

A plane at specified angles to two reference planes may be

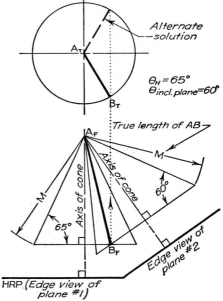

It is necessary to draw the base of only one cone true size in order to obtain a second view of the line.

$\theta_H = 65°$
$\theta_{incl. plane} = 60°$

FIG. 142. A line making specified angles with any two planes.

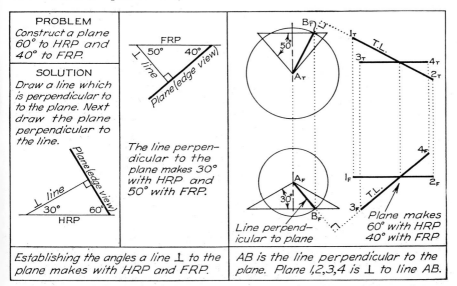

PROBLEM		
Construct a plane 60° to HRP and 40° to FRP.		
SOLUTION		
Draw a line which is perpendicular to the plane. Next draw the plane perpendicular to the line.	*The line perpendicular to the plane makes 30° with HRP and 50° with FRP.*	*Plane makes 60° with HRP 40° with FRP*
Establishing the angles a line ⊥ to the plane makes with HRP and FRP.	*AB is the line perpendicular to the plane. Plane 1,2,3,4 is ⊥ to line AB.*	

FIG. 143. Constructing a plane making specified angles with two reference planes.

readily obtained by drawing it perpendicular to a constructed line which shall be perpendicular to the desired plane. The plane of Fig. 143 has a line perpendicular to it at 30° to HRP and 50° to FRP. First construct the line AB which shall be perpendicular to the plane by means of the two cones on which it lies as explained in Art. 107. Next, draw a plane perpendicular to the line AB by means of intersecting true-length frontal and horizontal lines.

110. A LINE CONNECTING TWO SKEW LINES AT SPECIFIED ANGLES TO THE LINES

The solution to this problem is based on the straight line of intersection of two cones having a common vertex. It is necessary to find the true length of *both* given lines in the same view. Since the method of solution requires one line to be in its point view in one view, the true-length view of the lines should be obtained by finding one line in its point view and taking the line of sight for the next auxiliary view perpendicular to the other line (AB of Fig. 144) where *both* lines will appear true length. Note that AB and CE are both true length in the secondary auxiliary views of parts 2 and 4 of Fig. 144.

Draw two *intersecting* lines parallel to the two true-length lines A_oB_o and C_oE_o as shown in part 3 of Fig. 144. At the intersection S_o of these two lines draw the triangular views of the two cones with the two lines as their axes. The vertex of each cone will be at S_o, and the elements of *both* cones will be of equal length. *Assume* a length of elements. The straight line of intersection RS of the two cones will be *parallel* to the answer. Since line CE appears in its point view in one view, it will be necessary to draw the point view of the line in part 3 parallel to the true length of CE. In the point view of CE in part 4 draw that view of the answer parallel to R_AS_A of part 3. This view will locate P_A, which will be projected to the secondary auxiliary view. Through P_o draw P_oO_o parallel to R_oS_o of part 3. Two views of the answer have been obtained. See Arts. 73 to 76 for other lines connecting two skew lines.

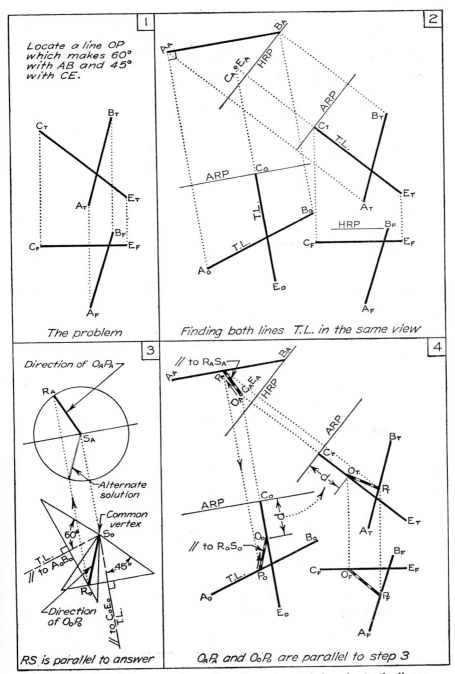

1

Locate a line OP
which makes 60°
with AB and 45°
with CE.

The problem

2

Finding both lines T.L. in the same view

3

Direction of $O_A P_A$

Alternate solution

Common vertex

60°

45°

T.L. // to $A_o B_o$

Direction of $O_o P_o$

to $C_o E_o$ T.L.

RS is parallel to answer

4

// to $R_A S_A$

ARP

HRP

// to $R_o S_o$

T.L.

$O_A P_A$ and $O_o P_o$ are parallel to step 3

FIG. 144. A line connecting two skew lines at specified angles to the lines.

111. REVOLVING A LINE ABOUT A LINE

Each end of the line, as it revolves about the other line as an axis, revolves in the path of a circle perpendicular to the axis. As shown in Fig. 145 each end of the line usually has its own radius of path of revolution. The point view of the axis determines the radii of the circles of revolution. The gorge circle of Fig. 145 is the circle of revolution for the *closest point R* of line AB to the axis CE.

In the point view of CE in Fig. 146, A_T and B_T have their own circles of revolution. The gorge circle may be drawn tangent to $A_T B_T$ with the perpendicular

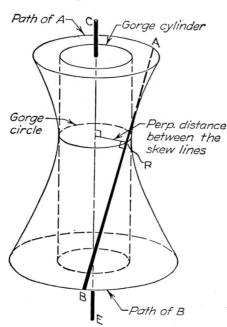

FIG. 145. Revolving a line about a line.

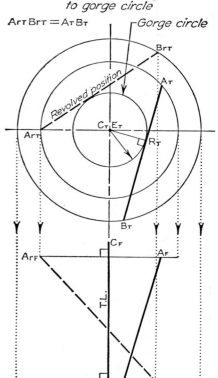

FIG. 146. Revolving a line about a line.

distance from the point view of CE to A_TB_T as the radius. The revolved position $A_{rT}B_{rT}$ of A_TB_T is tangent to the gorge circle and equal in length to A_TB_T.

Another method establishing the revolved position of the revolved line in the view containing the point view of the axis is shown in Fig. 147. The line connecting the point view of the axis to A_T is revolved through $\alpha°$ to A_{rT}. The line connecting the point view of the axis to B_T likewise revolves through the same angle α. And so does R_T. The distances d and d_1 of the ends of the line on either side of R_T remain the same in the revolved position. Only inaccuracies or errors will prevent either or both of these items from being correct.

The length of the revolved position of the line relative to the regular view of the line varies in all views except the point view of the axis.

In Fig. 148 line AB is revolved about line CE as the axis. The revolved position of AB is first obtained in the auxiliary view with B_{rA} in its farthest forward position. Since C_FE_F is true length in the front view, the paths of revolution appear as lines perpendicular to C_FE_F. A_{rF} and B_{rF} are projected to the top view. Note that each revolved position is on its own ellipse in the top view.

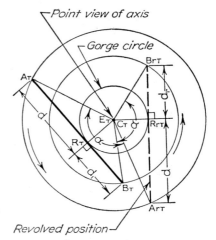

FIG. 147. Revolving a line about a line.

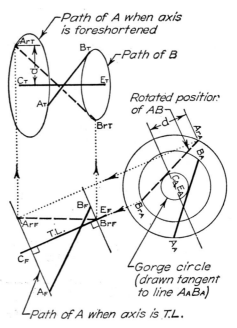

FIG. 148. Revolving a line about a line.

112. TRUE SIZE OF A PLANE BY REVOLUTION

The true size of a plane may determined by revolving it about a true-length line of the plane and into the reference plane containing the true-length line. The true-length lines are frontal, horizontal, and profile lines of the plane being revolved.

In Fig. 149 plane ABC is revolved about the true-length line BE as the axis of revolution. Points A and C both have their own circle of revolution which is perpendicular to the axis BE. The plane ABC is revolved until every point of it is in the indicated reference plane.

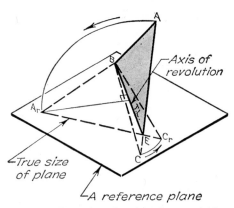

FIG. 149. True size of a plane by revolution.

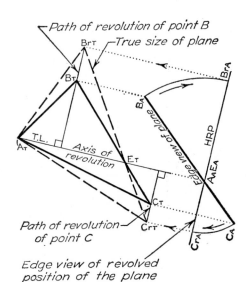

FIG. 150. True size of a plane by revolution.

In Fig. 150 the added line $A_T E_T$ on plane ABC is the true-length line which is used as the axis of revolution. The point view of the axis and edge view of the plane will be the circular view of the paths of revolution of the *individual* corners of the plane. The edge views of the paths of revolution appear perpendicular to the axis when the axis is true length. The auxiliary view shows that each corner was revolved into the HRP containing the axis AE.

113. REVOLVING A PLANE TO AVOID OVERLAPPING OF VIEWS

Another line added to the plane *parallel* to the true-length line intended to be used as the axis of revolution of the plane may also be used as the axis of revolution.

In Fig. 151 the true-length line $C_F E_F$ was the true-length line intended to be used as the axis of revolution. However, to have used it would have meant that the revolved true-size view of the plane ABC would have overlapped the top view of the plane (see Fig. 150 as an example of the overlapping). A line *parallel* to $C_F E_F$ is added to the plane through the extreme corner B_F and used as the axis. The plane is revolved in a direction to *avoid* overlapping, thus making the drawing *easier* to read.

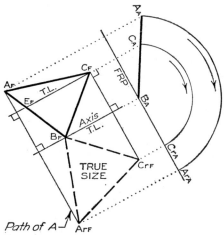

FIG. 151. Revolving a plane to avoid overlapping of views.

114. ADDING A FIGURE TO A PLANE BY COUNTERREVOLUTION

Any figure or shape to be added to a plane by counterrevolution is added *in* the revolved true-size view of the plane and then revolved back to the regular views of the plane.

In Fig. 152 plane $ABCD$ has been revolved about a line through A_R parallel to the true-length profile line $B_R M_R$. The plane $ABCD$ has been revolved into PRP and is true size in the side view. The paths of revolution will, of course, be perpendicular to the true-length view of the axis. The triangle $1_{rR}2_{rR}3_{rR}$ has been added to the revolved true-size view of the plane. The three corners of the triangle are then projected to the *revolved* position of the plane in the auxiliary view and then revolved to the edge view of the plane. Follow each corner from view to view with a pencil in the direction of the arrows.

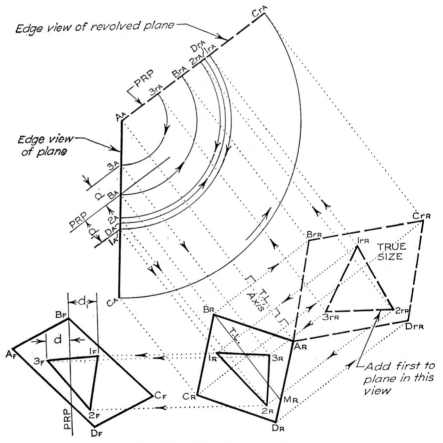

Fig. 152. Adding lines to a plane.

115. REVOLVING A PLANE ABOUT A LINE OBLIQUE TO THE PLANE

A plane revolving about a line oblique to the plane is similar to one skew line revolving about another skew line, because the plane is represented by lines. In the point view of the axis RS of Fig. 153, point A has been revolved to its farthest forward position. Since the plane is represented by a triangle, only two gorge circles are needed. The paths of revolution of the individual corners appear in their edge views and are perpendicular to the axis when the axis is true length.

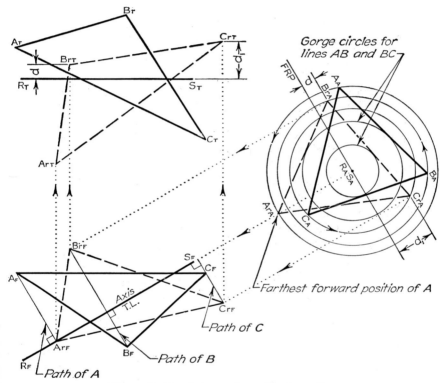

FIG. 153. Revolving a plane about any line.

116. REVOLVING AN OBLIQUE PLANE TO A HORIZONTAL POSITION ABOUT TWO PERPENDICULAR AXES

The plane must be revolved about one axis until it reaches an inclined position in the point view of the other axis. The inclined position of the plane is then revolved about the second axis to a horizontal position.

The industrial adjustable angle plate of Fig. 154 to which a part is attached has its angles established by the sine bar principle. The sine

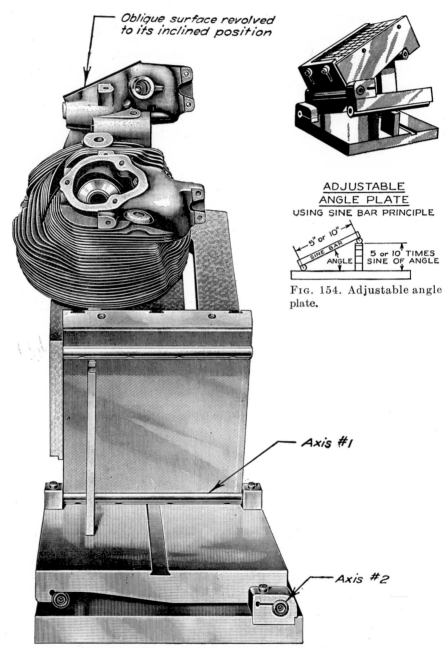

Oblique surface revolved to its inclined position

ADJUSTABLE
ANGLE PLATE
USING SINE BAR PRINCIPLE

5" or 10"
SINE BAR
ANGLE
5 or 10 TIMES
SINE OF ANGLE

Fig. 154. Adjustable angle plate.

Axis #1

Axis #2

Fig. 155. Oblique plane revolved to its inclined position.

of the angle is set by gage blocks which are accurate to a few millionths of an inch. Several blocks are stacked together to make any desired measurement. Note the two axes of revolution for the plates and that they are perpendicular to each other.

Figure 155 shows one step in the revolution of one surface of an aircraft cylinder block being revolved from an oblique position to a horizontal position. This job required the angles to be furnished to seconds of a degree, which is greater than graphical accuracy allows. *After* the problem was solved graphically, the angles were computed mathematically and based on the triangles of the graphical solution.

Figure 156 shows the method of determining the angle for the first step of the revolution process, which is determining the inclined position of the plane. The true-length line $B_F E_F$ added to the plane in the point view of axis 1 will, when revolved about axis 1 to its horizontal position, appear as a point in the side view. The revolved position of the plane $ABCD$ appears in its edge view in the side view and contains the point

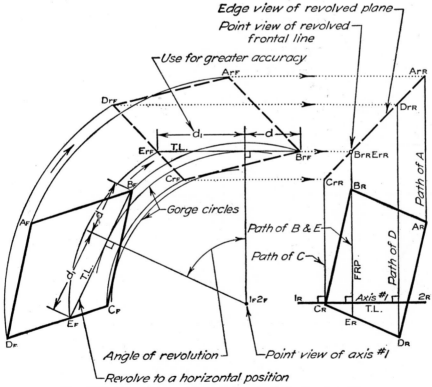

Fig. 156. Revolving an oblique plane to its inclined position.

view of the revolved true-length
line $B_F E_F$. Note the use of the
measurements d and d_1 of $B_F E_F$
in the revolved position of this
line. They increase the graphical accuracy. Note the use of
the gorge circles.

Figure 157 shows the inclined
position of the plane revolved
about axis 2 to its horizontal
position. The two angles of
revolution are so labeled in Figs.
156 and 157.

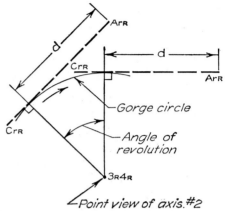

FIG. 157. Revolving the inclined position
of an oblique plane to its horizontal position.

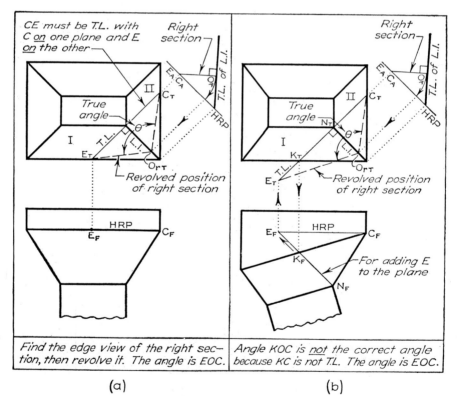

Find the edge view of the right section, then revolve it. The angle is EOC.

Angle KOC is *not* the correct angle
because KC is not T.L. The angle is EOC.

(a)   (b)

FIG. 158. Obtaining the angle between two planes by revolution.

117. ANGLE BETWEEN TWO PLANES BY REVOLUTION OF THE RIGHT SECTION

The right section will appear in its edge view when the line of intersection is true length and may be revolved about a horizontal, frontal, or profile line of the right section as an axis until the plane is true size in a regular view. In Fig. 158a line $C_T E_T$ is a horizontal line so chosen that point C is on one plane and E on the other plane and $C_T E_T$ appears in the top view *perpendicular* to the line of intersection. This line *must be true length* and will appear in its point view in the auxiliary view. The right section is drawn through the point view of $C_A E_A$ perpendicular to the line of intersection. Point O will be on the line of intersection and becomes the vertex of the angle. In revolving O_A about $C_A E_A$ to the horizontal, the true angle between planes 1 and 2 will be $C_T O_{rT} E_T$.

In Fig. 158a points C and E may easily be placed on their respective planes and in the same horizontal plane as the front view indicates. In Fig. 158b point K corresponds to E of Fig. 158a except that, as the front view indicates, point K is *not* in the same *HRP* as point C. Line $K_F N_F$ has been added to plane 1, and when it is extended to where it intersects with the *HRP* through C at E_F, point E will be on the *same HRP* as C, thus making $C_T E_T$ true length in the top view. The remainder of the solution is the same as that of Fig. 158a. $C_T O_{rT} E_T$ is the true angle.

CHAPTER 8

FORCE DIAGRAMS

118. VECTOR OR FORCE DIAGRAMS: THE RESULTANT

In Fig. 159a the loads OR and OS are measured along the respective members in their *true-length* views using some convenient scale of a specified number of pounds per inch. The scaled length of force is *independent* of the physical length of the member. The diagonal of the parallelogram formed by the use of the two known forces is the resultant OK. Point O will move along OK with the intensity of load of OK. The same scale used to lay out OR and OS is used to measure it.

In Fig. 159b the forces applied along the diagonals in the *opposite* direction to the forces of the two members of each parallelogram establishes equilibrium.

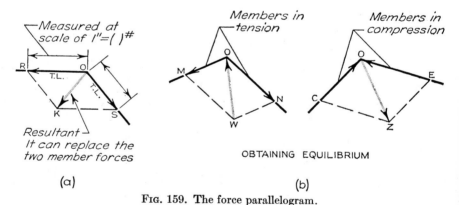

OBTAINING EQUILIBRIUM

(a)   (b)

FIG. 159. The force parallelogram.

119. ESTABLISHING THE LOAD CREATED IN OTHER MEMBERS BY THE KNOWN LOAD IN ONE MEMBER

The forces of Fig. 160 are called **concurrent coplanar forces** because they all lie in one plane and intersect at a common point.

The known force may, if the problem requires it, be placed and scaled along the extension of the member as indicated in Fig. 160. OE is equal in length to OA and is in the same direction. The force EO serves as the diagonal of a parallelogram based on the direction of the other two members. After the parallelogram has been drawn, OM and ON in their true-length views will be the forces created in these two members by the load applied to OA. The system of the three members is in equilibrium.

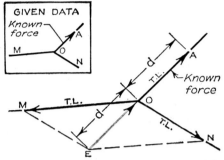

Fɪɢ. 160. Obtaining the forces created in members by another force.

120. OBTAINING THE RESULTANT OF THREE CONCURRENT NONCOPLANAR FORCES

Forces are noncoplanar when they do not all lie in the same plane.

A parallelepiped may be formed by the loads in the three members as shown pictorially in Fig. 161a. When these three members are placed in an orthographic drawing, some or all of the members may not be true length in the regular views. The loads may be scaled along the members *only* in their true-length auxiliary views or revolved true-length views.

After the loads have been properly scaled along the individual members using a scale convenient to all members, the parallelepiped may be drawn

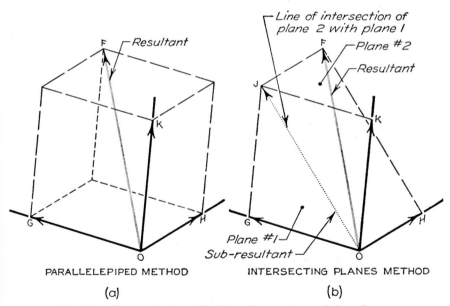

Fɪɢ. 161. Two methods of obtaining the resultant of three forces.

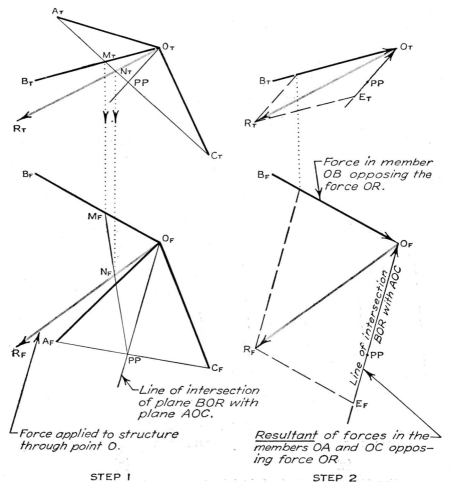

FIG. 162. Application of a resultant force.

Resultant force

Tangential force

Cutting tool

Feed force

Radial force

Components of the total load are measured by strain gages

Line of intersection of plane BOR with plane AOC.

Force applied to structure through point O.

STEP 1

Force in member OB opposing the force OR.

Line of intersection BOR with AOC

Resultant of forces in the members OA and OC opposing force OR

STEP 2

FIG. 163a. Determining by the intersecting-plane method the opposing forces created in three members by a given force.

110

in each orthographic view entirely *independent* of the foreshortening of the lengths of the individual members.   The fact that equal-length parallel lines foreshorten equally makes this possible.   After the parallelepiped has been drawn, the diagonal through O, which is the resultant, may be revolved for its true length or an auxiliary view may be drawn for the same purpose.

Figure 161*b* shows a different method of determining the resultant of the *same* three forces shown in Fig. 161*a*. OJ is the resultant of the two forces OG and OK.   It may be considered to be replacing these two forces. This subresultant (it is not the total resultant) and force OH when combined in a parallelogram will produce the resultant OF of all three forces and will give the same answer arrived at in Fig. 161*a*.

The two parallelograms are spatially two planes with OJ, which is the subresultant, as the line of intersection of the two planes.   A full under-

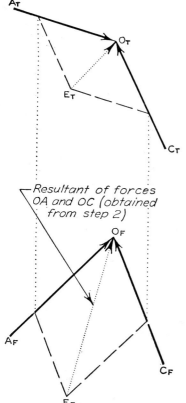

Resultant of forces
OA and OC (obtained
from step 2)

STEP 3

standing of these two planes and the line of intersection OJ is essential to the solution of the problem of Figs. 163*a* and *b*.

Figure 162 shows an application of the forces applied to a cutting tool.

121. DETERMINING BY THE INTERSECTING-PLANE METHOD THE OPPOSING FORCES CREATED IN THREE MEMBERS BY AN APPLIED FORCE

The applied force of Fig. 163*a* is OR. This force creates opposing equilibrium forces in the three members OA, OB, and OC.   The applied force OR and *any* one of the three members will be plane 2 shown in Fig. 161*b*. BOR is plane 2, and AOC plane 1, which is composed of the other two members.   The piercing point of line AC of plane AOC with plane BOR has been labeled PP.   The line of intersection of plane 1 with plane 2 is $O\text{-}PP$, which corresponds to OJ of Fig. 161*b*.

For the sake of clarity, plane 2, including the line of intersection $O\text{-}PP$, has been redrawn as shown in step 2.   The parallelogram which was constructed with OR

FIG. 163*b*. Determining by the intersecting-plane method the opposing forces created in three members by a given force.

as the diagonal establishes the opposing force in member *OB*. The opposing force *OE* along the line of intersection is the subresultant *OJ* shown in Fig. 161*b*. This force is the resultant of the opposing forces of the members *OA* and *OC*. In step 3 the opposing forces in *OA* and *OC* are obtained from the parallelogram formed by these members with *OE* as the diagonal. In steps 2 and 3 *either* the top or the front view of each parallelogram may be drawn first. Each corner of the parallelogram *must* project orthographically from view to view. The true lengths of the opposing forces may be found by applying either method of determining the true length of a line.

CHAPTER 9

POINT, LINE, AND PLANE RELATIONS WITH CYLINDERS, CONES, AND SPHERES

122. A CYLINDER

A cylinder is a surface generated by moving a straight line in such a way that it always touches a *curved* line and is parallel to its original position. The curved line, although it usually is a circle, may be a parabola (see Fig. 197), a hyperbola, cycloid, or *any* curved line as illustrated in Fig. 164. All cylinders referred to in this book will be circular cylinders unless stated to the contrary.

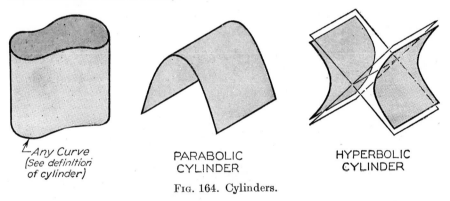

Any Curve
(See definition
of cylinder)

PARABOLIC
CYLINDER

HYPERBOLIC
CYLINDER

Fig. 164. Cylinders.

123. ELEMENTS OF A CIRCULAR CYLINDER

Each position of the straight line as it generates the cylinder is called a **straight-line element.** The circles that may be drawn on the surface of circular cylinders are called **circular elements.** The **contour elements** are the two straight-line elements which form part of the outline of a view of a cylinder.

124. RIGHT AND OBLIQUE CIRCULAR CYLINDERS

Figure 165*a* shows two right circular cylinders formed by round coins. Since the circles of the coins are perpendicular to the axes of the cylinders, the cylinders are called **right circular cylinders.**

In Fig. 165*b* the circular edges of the coins are at acute angles to the axes of the two cylinders. Cylinders thus formed are called **oblique circular cylinders.**

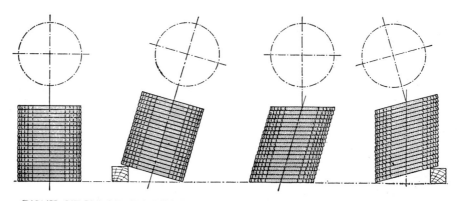

RIGHT CIRCULAR CYLINDERS　　　　OBLIQUE CIRCULAR CYLINDERS

(a)　　　　　　　　　　　　　　　　　　　　　　(b)

This Illustration is From
GEOMETRY OF SHEET METAL WORK
*by Permission of A. Dickson, Author
and Sir Isaac Pitman & Sons, Ltd., London, Publisher*

FIG. 165. Circular cylinders.

125. A CONE

A **cone** is a surface generated by moving a straight line in such a way that it always touches a *curved line* and contains a fixed point called the **vertex** which does not lie in the plane of the curve. Although the curved line usually is a circle, it may be a parabola, hyperbola, or *any* curved line as shown in Fig. 166. All cones referred to in this book will be circular cones unless stated to the contrary.

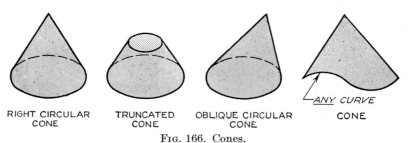

RIGHT CIRCULAR　　TRUNCATED　　OBLIQUE CIRCULAR　　ANY CURVE
CONE　　　　　　　CONE　　　　　　CONE　　　　　　　CONE

FIG. 166. Cones.

126. RIGHT AND OBLIQUE CIRCULAR CONES

A right circular cone has a circular base which is perpendicular to the axis of the cone that extends from the vertex to the center of the base. An oblique circular cone has a circular base that is not perpendicular to the axis of the cone (see Figs. 273, 279, 280, 306c, and 307 for applications of oblique cones).

127. ELEMENTS OF A CIRCULAR CONE

The straight-line elements extend from the vertex to the base of the cone, while the circular elements are parallel to the circular base as shown in Fig. 167c. The contour elements are the two straight-line elements which form part of the outline of a view of a cone.

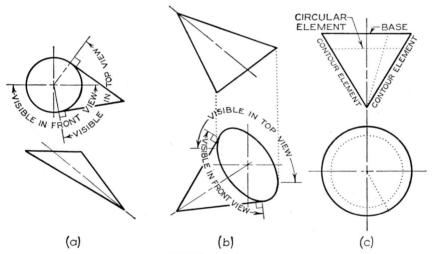

Fig. 167. Visibility of elements on cones.

128. VISIBILITY OF ELEMENTS FOR A GIVEN VIEW OF A CONE OR CYLINDER

The straight-line elements of the cone of Fig. 167a which are visible in the front view are those which end on the front half of the base in the top view. The visible straight-line elements in the top view are those ending on the base between the *apparent* points of tangency of the contour elements with the base of the cone in that view.

In Fig. 167b the visible straight-line elements in the front view are those which end on the elliptical view of the base between the *apparent* tangency points of the contour elements with the base of the cone in that view.

In Fig. 167b the visible elements for the top view are determined in the front view as being between the tangency points of the two vertical projection lines shown on the drawing. The exact point of tangency may be located by referring to Art. 144.

The visibility of the elements of a cylinder may be determined in a similar manner, the only difference being that the two contour elements of the cylinder are parallel instead of converging at a vertex.

129. LOCATING A POINT ON A CONE OR CYLINDER

Figure 168 shows that a point on a circular cone is on one straight-line and one circular element. Either will locate the point on the cone. See Fig. 169 for orthographic views of the point, the straight-line, and circular elements containing the point and the cone.

A point on a cylinder may be similarly located.

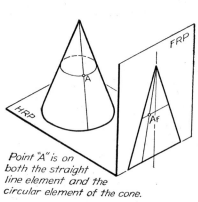

Point "A" is on both the straight line element and the circular element of the cone.

FIG. 168. A point on a cone.

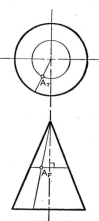

Regardless of whether point "A" is given in the top or front view, the other view of point "A" may be located by either the straight line or circular element containing the point.

FIG. 169. A point on a cone.

130. A PLANE WHICH IS TANGENT TO A CYLINDER OR CONE AND CONTAINS A POINT ON THE SURFACE

Any plane which is tangent to a cylinder and contains a point on the cylinder will be tangent to the cylinder along the straight-line element through the point. The plane will also intersect the plane of the base of the cylinder in a line tangent to the base at that end of the tangent element.

In Fig. 170a, MN is the tangent element containing the point G. RS is the line of intersection of the plane with the base plane at point N of element MN.

In Fig. 170*b*, the line of tangency of the plane tangent to the cone through point *E* is the straight-line element *VC*. The intersection of the plane with the base of the cone is line *AB* and is tangent to the base at point *C* of element *VC*.

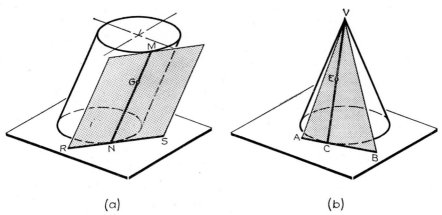

(a)   (b)

FIG. 170. Planes tangent to a cylinder and cone.

131. A LINE TANGENT TO A CIRCLE OR OTHER PLANE CURVE

A line spatially tangent to a circle or other plane curve *must* be in the *plane* of the circle or curve (see Fig. 171). Line $A_T B_T$ of Fig. 171*b* is only *apparently* tangent to the circle.

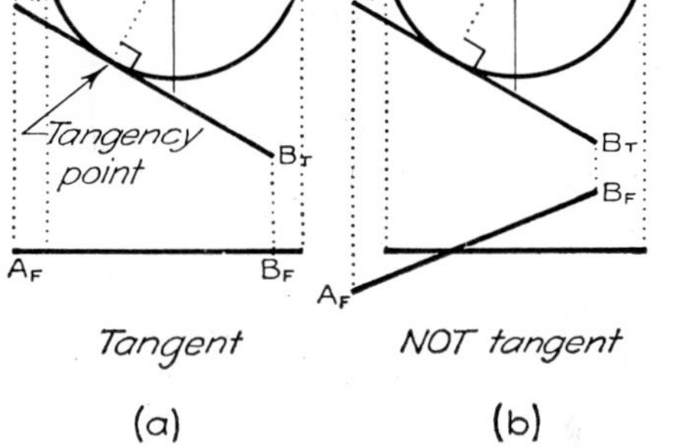

A line to be tangent to a circle (or any other plane curve) must lie in the plane of the circle (or curve).

Tangency point

A_F B_F

A_T B_T

B_F

A_F

Tangent   NOT tangent

(a)   (b)

FIG. 171. Line tangent to a circle.

132. CONSTRUCTING A PLANE TANGENT TO A CYLINDER AND PARALLEL TO A GIVEN LINE

A plane which contains the given line and is parallel to the elements of the cylinder will be parallel to the desired plane. In Fig. 172 plane ABK is parallel to the desired plane. Line BK is the line of intersection of the plane with the base plane of the cylinder. RS drawn parallel to BK and line MN through the tangency point N will represent a plane tangent to the cylinder and parallel to AB.

Figure 173 is an orthographic solution of a similar problem.

133. A PLANE TANGENT TO A CONE AND PARALLEL TO A GIVEN OBLIQUE LINE

A line through the vertex of the cone and parallel to the given line will be one line of the desired plane. A second line of the desired plane will contain the point where the line through the vertex pierces the base plane of the cone and will be tangent to the base of the cone. The first line of this plane corresponds to line AB of Fig. 174, and the second line corresponds to line ED.

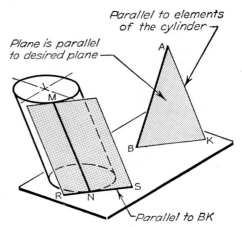

Fig. 172. Plane parallel to a line and tangent to a cylinder.

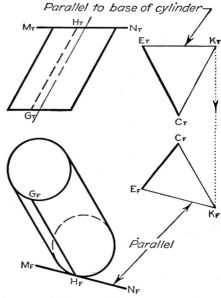

Fig. 173. Plane parallel to a line and tangent to a cylinder.

134. ESTABLISHING A PLANE CONTAINING A GIVEN OBLIQUE LINE AT A SPECIFIED ANGLE TO A REFERENCE PLANE

A cone whose elements make a specified angle with its base plane will be tangent to the desired plane when the vertex of the cone is placed on the line and the base of the cone is in or parallel to the reference plane.

The cone referred to is shown in Fig. 174 with the vertex at point A of the given line AB. Line AB pierces the reference plane containing the base of the cone, and line DE is tangent to the base at point C.

In Fig. 175 line AB is the given line and Θ_H the specified angle. AB pierces the base plane of the cone at E. Line EC is tangent to the base of the cone, and A_TC_T is the tangent element. Note the alternate solution. B_TK_T is incorrect because the line does *not* lie in the base plane of the cone.

In Fig. 176 a plane containing

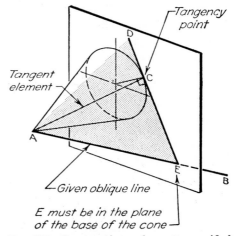

FIG. 174. Constructing a plane at a specified angle to a reference plane and containing an oblique line.

the given line AB was constructed at the angle of Θ_F to FRP. Both BM and EC are correct second lines for the plane, since both are tangent to circles of the cone.

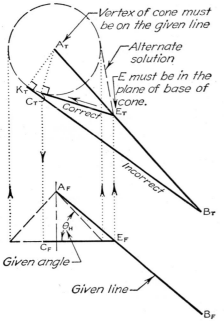

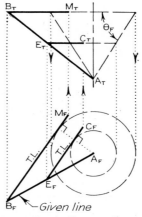

FIG. 176. (*Above*) Constructing a plane at a specified angle to FRP and containing an oblique line.

FIG. 175. (*Left*) Constructing a plane at a specified angle to HRP and containing an oblique line.

In Fig. 177 the given *inclined* line AB corresponds with line DE of Fig. 174 and Θ_F is the specified angle that the plane is to make with FRP. In order to find point C as a third point of the plane, arbitrarily choose C_F and draw the circular view of the cone tangent to line AB with C_F as the center of the circle. Draw the top view of the cone by first locating the base in the top view in the FRP containing AB and then drawing the contour elements at their specified Θ_F angle. The contour elements locate the top view of C_F which establishes the plane.

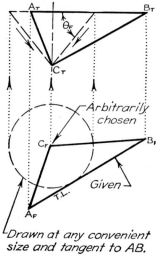

Given: Line AB and Θ_F.
Req'd: To draw a plane
containing AB and making
Θ_F with FRP.
Answer: Plane ABC.

Drawn at any convenient
size and tangent to AB.

FIG. 177. Constructing a plane at a specified angle to FRP and containing a given inclined line.

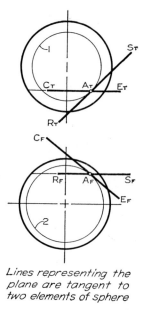

Lines representing the
plane are tangent to
two elements of sphere

FIG. 178. Plane tangent to a sphere.

135. A PLANE TANGENT TO A SPHERE AT A POINT ON THE SPHERE

Line RS of Fig. 178 is tangent to a horizontal circle on the sphere through the given point A (see Fig. 183). Line CE is tangent to a frontal circle on the sphere through A. Lines RS and CE represent the desired tangent plane. See Art. 67 for another method of determining the same plane.

136. A PLANE TANGENT TO A PARABOLOID

Figure 179a shows the construction of a line tangent to a parabolic element of the paraboloid. There is a parabola through point A, and it is the same size as the parabolic contour element of the front view.

Revolve A to its revolved position A_{rF}, and draw a line tangent to the parabola by using the d measurement as indicated to find B on the axis of the paraboloid. AB will be one line of the plane. Another is a line tangent to the circular element 1 through A as shown in Fig. 179b.

137. PIERCING POINTS OF A LINE WITH A CYLINDER

Construct a plane containing the given line AB of Fig. 180a, and make it parallel to the cylinder by drawing the line AS parallel to the elements of the cylinder. This plane will intersect the cylinder along the two straight-line elements which contain the piercing points. The plane intersects a base plane along line SW. Line SW inter-

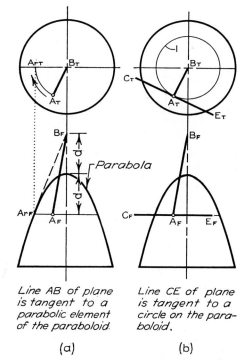

Line AB of plane is tangent to a parabolic element of the paraboloid.

Line CE of plane is tangent to a circle on the paraboloid.

(a)   (b)

FIG. 179. Plane tangent to a paraboloid.

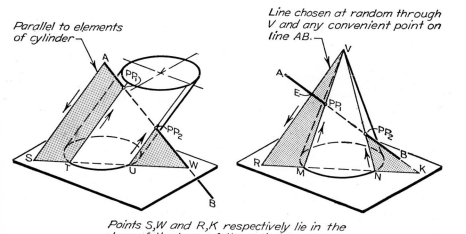

Parallel to elements of cylinder

Line chosen at random through V and any convenient point on line AB.

Points S,W and R,K respectively lie in the plane of the base of the cylinder and cone

(a)   (b)

FIG. 180. Piercing points of a line with a cylinder and a cone.

sects the base of the cylinder at points T and U, which are ends of the elements containing the piercing points. The piercing points PP_1 and PP_2 are located where line AB intersects the elements through T and U.

138. PIERCING POINTS OF A LINE WITH A CONE

A plane containing the vertex of the cone and the given line will intersect the base of the cone at two points. These two points are the ends of the two straight-line elements of the cone on which the piercing points lie. The plane of Fig. 180b is VAB. Line AB pierces the base plane at point K. A line VA would have pierced the base plane beyond the confines of the illustration. Line VE of the plane also pierces the base plane at point R. RK intersects the base of the cone at M and N, which are ends of two straight-line elements containing the piercing points. The piercing points PP_1 and PP_2 are located where the elements MV and NV intersect line AB.

Figure 181 shows a second method of finding the piercing points of a line piercing a cone. First draw line $V_F E_F$ parallel to the base of the cone. Line AB pierces the plane of the base at point K. A line through K_T parallel to $V_T E_T$ will locate the lower end of the elements containing the two piercing points. The piercing points are where these two elements intersect line AB.

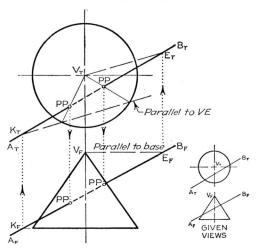

FIG. 181. Finding the piercing points of a line with a cone: second method.

139. PRACTICAL APPLICATION OF A LINE PIERCING A CONE

Lines AB and CE of Fig. 182 represent the center lines of two long pipes at 30% grade which carry water along a mountainside and generally conform to the surface of the mountain. A pipe of 30% grade is needed to connect these two pipes. The connecting pipe may be assumed to be an element of a 30% grade cone whose vertex is along line AB. The other end of the connecting pipe will be where line CE pierces the 30% grade cone. *Assume* B to be the vertex of the cone. A plane containing B and the line CE is found to intersect the base of the cone along line MN.

Compare this plane and its intersection MN with plane $VAEB$ of Fig. 180 and its intersection RK.

The intersection line MN intersects the base of the cone at K.   Line CE pierces the cone where it intersects the element KB.   If the line BP does not conform reasonably well to the surface of the mountain, another point along line AB should be chosen as the vertex of the cone. BP is

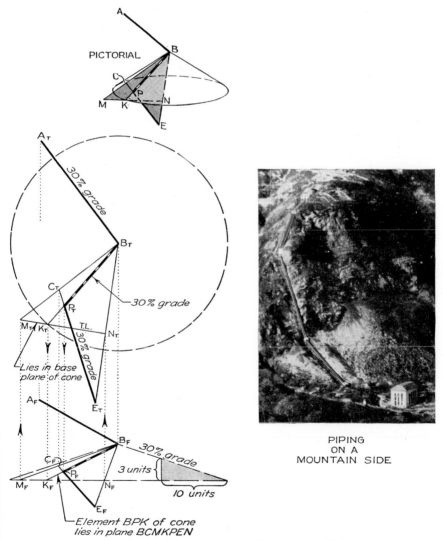

PIPING
ON A
MOUNTAIN SIDE

Fig. 182. Application of a line piercing a cone (line at a specified grade connecting two skew lines).

not likely to be the shortest connection at 30% grade.   For the shortest connection see Fig. 101.   However, it is not likely to conform to the surface of the mountain.

140. LOCATING A POINT ON A SPHERE

A point that is given in one view on a sphere may be located in another view by revolving it about vertical or horizontal axes of the sphere as shown in Fig. 183.   The circular view of the horizontal circle containing point P_T will appear in its horizontal edge view in the front view.   The frontal circle containing point P_T which appears as a horizontal line in the top view appears as a circle in the front view. There will be two solutions unless the point is specified as visible or invisible in the top view.

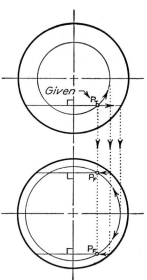

FIG. 183. Locating a point on a sphere.

CHAPTER 10

CONIC SECTIONS AND THEIR APPLICATIONS

141. CONIC SECTIONS

The sections of a cone cut by a plane are a circle, an ellipse, a parabola, and a hyperbola. These sections are called **conic sections.** The plane of the circle is parallel to the circular base of the cone. The others are shown pictorially in Fig. 184.

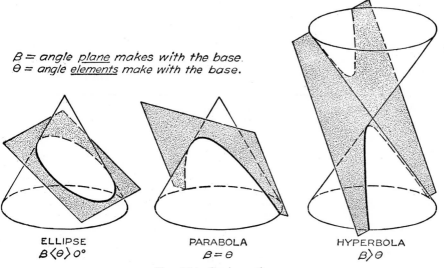

β = angle _plane_ makes with the base.
θ = angle _elements_ make with the base.

ELLIPSE
$\beta \langle \theta \rangle 0°$

PARABOLA
$\beta = \theta$

HYPERBOLA
$\beta \rangle \theta$

Fig. 184. Conic sections.

Figure 185 shows orthographically the conic sections, the angles of the section planes necessary to obtain the various sections, and the spheres tangent to the cones and planes which are used to obtain the focal points of the conic sections.

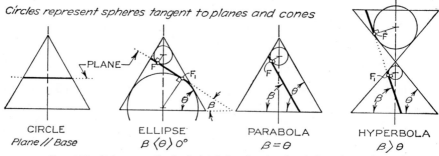

FIG. 185. Sphere method of obtaining focal points of conic sections.

142. THE ELLIPSE

The ellipse is a very commonly used conic section. All foreshortened views of a circle are ellipses. The edge view, of course, is a straight line. *All* ellipses may be considered as foreshortened circles equal in diameter to the major axis of the ellipse.

When the major and minor axes of the ellipse are known, either of two commonly used methods of plotting points on the curve may be used.

The concentric circle method shown in Fig. 186a uses two concentric circles with the major and minor diameters of the ellipse as the diameters of the circles. Radial lines cross both circles at a series of points such as T and R. The point of intersection S of a line through point T parallel to one axis with a line through point R parallel to the other axis is a point on the ellipse.

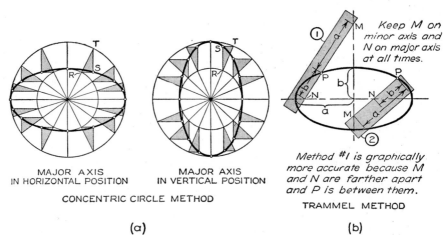

FIG. 186. Two methods of obtaining points on ellipses.

The trammel method of locating points on the ellipse is explained in Fig. 186*b*. Point *M* of the trammel is *always* placed on the minor axis, and point *N* of the trammel is *always* placed on the major axis.

143. LOCATING THE CENTER AND AXES OF A GIVEN ELLIPSE

In locating the center of an ellipse on a wood or metal cylinder, draw two sets of parallel lines *AB*, *CE* and 1-2, 3-4 on the surface of the object as shown in Fig. 187. Connect the midpoints of the two pairs of parallel lines to form the lines *M*, *N*, and 7-8. Their intersection point *O* is the center of the ellipse. The proof of this is shown in the reduced circular view of the ellipse.

After the center of the ellipse has been established, a circle of a convenient diameter may be drawn with its center at the center of the ellipse as shown in Fig. 188. Lines connecting the intersection of the circle with the ellipse will form a rectangle whose sides are parallel to the axes of the ellipse.

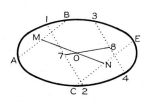
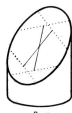

Lines connecting the mid-points of parallel lines will pass through the center of the ellipse.

Reduced circular view of ellipse (to left) and the parallel lines.

FIG. 187. Locating the center of a given ellipse.

Given: Ellipse and its center
Req'd: To find axes of ellipse

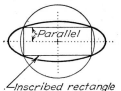

Draw circle of convenient size   *Inscribed rectangle*

FIG. 188. (*Right*) Locating the axes of a given ellipse.

The intersections of the circle with the ellipse are the corners of the inscribed rectangle. Axes of the ellipse are parallel to the sides of the rectangle.

144. LOCATING THE TANGENCY POINT OF A LINE TANGENT TO AN ELLIPSE

When the ellipse and the line (which *must* lie in the plane of the *ellipse*) are revolved about the major axis to the true size of the circle that created the ellipse as shown in Fig. 189, the revolved line will be tangent to the circle. Line *AB* extended to point *N on* the major axis (axis of revolution) also locates a point on the revolved position of the line. The tangency point TP_r where a line through point N is tangent to the circle may be readily found. The revolved TP may be revolved to the ellipse with the edge view of the path of revolution perpendicular to the axis of revolution. An application of this is given in Art. 98.

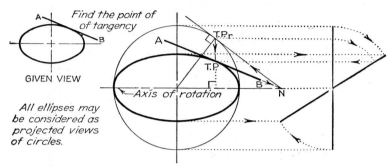

FIG. 189. Locating the tangency point of a line tangent to an ellipse.

145. ESTABLISHING THE MAJOR AND MINOR AXES OF ELLIPSES IN ORTHOGRAPHIC VIEWS

The axes of the ellipse in a view projected from the edge view of a circle are readily determined. The major axis appears in its point view at the center of the edge view of the circle and will be true length along the projection line in the auxiliary view (see $A_A B_A$ in Fig. 190). The minor axis is determined by projecting the two ends C_F and E_F of the edge view of the circle to the auxiliary view. The ellipse may be plotted by choosing points on the circle, projecting them to the edge view of the circle and from there to the auxiliary view, or by the concentric circle or

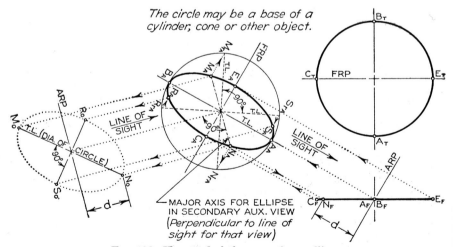

FIG. 190. How to find the axes of any ellipse.

trammel method. Four-center *approximate* ellipse methods **are** *not* accurate.

Note how the major axis of the ellipse of the secondary auxiliary view is located in the primary auxiliary view. The circular view of the ellipse is drawn in the primary auxiliary view. $M_A N_A$ is revolved about the major axis $B_A A_A$ to $M_{rA} N_{rA}$ on the circle. This is the true-size view of the major axis for the ellipse used in the secondary auxiliary view. The revolved position of the minor axis used in the secondary auxiliary view will also be true length and perpendicular to $M_{rA} N_{rA}$ in the primary auxiliary view. $S_{rA} R_{rA}$ will be the revolved minor axis. This line is then revolved about $B_A A_A$ to the ellipse as S_A and R_A, which are the primary auxiliary view positions of the ends of the minor axis used in the secondary auxiliary view. S_A and R_A are then projected to the secondary auxiliary view and become $S_o R_o$.

Figure 191 illustrates an application of Fig. 190 and is self-explanatory. Figure 196 shows an application of an ellipse.

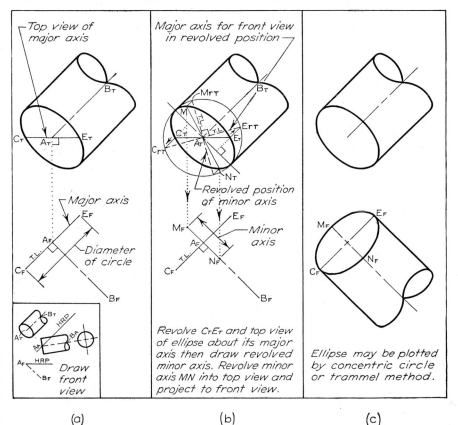

(a)   (b)   (c)

FIG. 191. Obtaining the axes of an ellipse.

146. THE PARABOLA

The parabola is a plane curve where each point is equidistant from a point called a **focal point** and a straight line in the plane called the **directrix** as shown in Fig. 192. Another method of drawing a parabola is self-explained in Fig. 193a.

A line tangent to a parabola through any point, such as D of Fig. 193b, on a parabola may be drawn by connecting point E on the axis of the parabola with point D. Point E is determined by measuring to the left of G the measurement b.

When the parabola is given and the directrix is not, the focal point may be found by the angle θ as indicated in Fig. 193b.

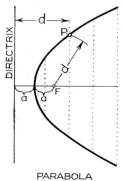

PARABOLA

Fig. 192. The parabola.

Given: A & B (measurements of a parabola)
Req'd: To draw the parabola

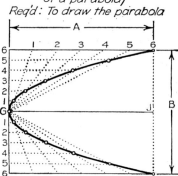

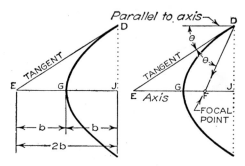

Divide the sides into equal parts as indicated. Draw one set of lines parallel to GJ and the other set converging at G. Points on the parabola may be found where lines through corresponding points intersect.

(a)

To find the focal point of a parabola draw a tangent line through D with EG = GJ. Then draw a line through D at angle of θ to the tangent.

(b)

Fig. 193. The parabola.

When the measurements of a parabola are the three measurements A, B, and C, the parabola may be constructed according to Fig. 194. An application of Figs. 193a and 194 is shown in Fig. 195.

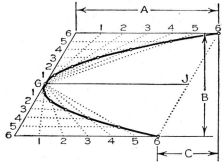

Given: A, B and C (measurements of
                    a parabola)
Req'd: To draw the parabola

Divide the sides into equal parts as indicated. Draw one set of lines parallel to GJ and the other set converging at G. Points on the parabola may be found where lines through corresponding points intersect.

FIG. 194. The twisted parabola.

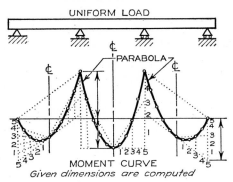

UNIFORM LOAD

PARABOLA

MOMENT CURVE
Given dimensions are computed

The parabolas may be drawn graphically by the indicated offset method.

FIG. 195. Applications of the parabola.

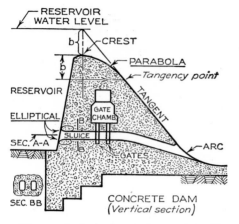

The parabola is drawn tangent to the
previously determined tangent. The tangency point is found by dimension "b"
being measured *below* the crest then
projecting over to the tangent. Note the
elliptical corners of the sluice.

(a)

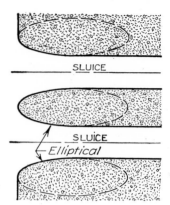

HORIZONTAL SECTION A-A
See preceding figure

Elliptical corners are
used to aid the flow of the
water through the sluice.
Sharp corners would
impede the flow.

(b)

FIG. 196. Application of the parabola and ellipse.

Figure 196 is an application of a parabola and an ellipse.   The parabola
(Fig. 196a), is constructed from the following data: (1) a line tangent to
the parabola and (2) the points corresponding to E and G of Fig. 193b.
The data of a parabola as this indicates are frequently different from
those data which may be readily substituted in a mathematical formula.

PARABOLIC FLUORESCENT
REFLECTOR
(*Tube placed at focal point*)

PARABOLA
(*cyl.*)

CEILING

PARALLEL RAYS
(*Concentrates
light evenly on
the picture*)

PICTURE

WALL

Figure 196b is an enlarged view of the
ellipse application of Fig. 196a.

Figure 197 is an application of a
parabola.   The surface of the reflector is
a parabolic cylinder (see Fig. 164).

FIG. 197. Application of the parabola.

147. THE HYPERBOLA

The hyperbola is a plane curve of the path of a point moving in such a manner that the difference of the distances of every position of the point from two fixed points called focal points is constant.

In Fig. 198, F and F_1 are the two fixed points and $2a$ the *constant* difference. The asymptotes of the hyperbola are determined by drawing a line from G perpendicular to the axis through the focal points to its intersection with a circle containing both focal points and the mid-point C as the center. Points M and C are two points on one asymptote.

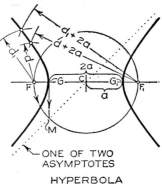

ONE OF TWO ASYMPTOTES

HYPERBOLA

Fig. 198. The hyperbola.

The data given for a hyperbola, as is also the case with other curves, is not always the standard data. Figure 199a shows the limited data for a hyperbola. Note how dimension a is used to determine point N and N in turn is used to determine point E as an additional point on an asymptote. Vertical lines through A and B to the asymptotes through C and E locate point M as also illustrated in Fig. 198. The focal points

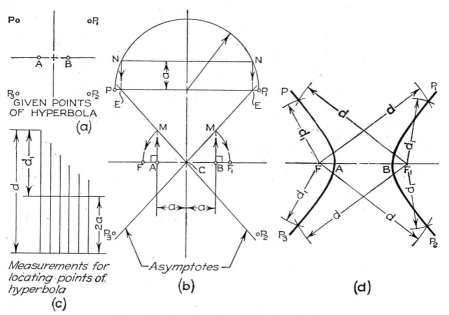

GIVEN POINTS OF HYPERBOLA

(a)

Measurements for locating points of hyperbola

(c)

Asymptotes

(b)

(d)

Fig. 199. Construction of the hyperbola.

may be determined by the arcs of radius CM.   Figure 199c shows a
simple method of determining the measurements d and d_1 for various
points on the curve of Figs. 198 and 199d.

Hyperbolas are used as a special grid formation in electrical graphs.
Figure 200 shows two common hyperbolic conic sections.

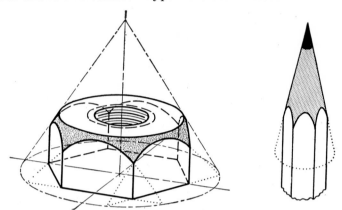

FIG. 200. Applications of the hyperbola.

CHAPTER 11

MINING, GEOLOGY, AND CIVIL ENGINEERING

148. CONTOUR LINES

In mining, geology, and civil engineering, contour maps (Fig. 201a) are commonly used. A contour line on a map is the intersection of a horizontal plane with the earth's surface. Therefore, every point of a given contour line has the same elevation. The series of contour lines of a map are taken at various elevations, depending upon the ruggedness of the terrain and the use of the map. The contour lines on maps may vary from 1-ft. elevation intervals to 50-ft. elevation intervals. In Fig. 201b the 870-ft. contour line lies in its horizontal plane. The 910-ft. contour line may also be plotted on the same plane and then raised 40 ft. for a pictorial. Figure 201c shows a completed pictorial.

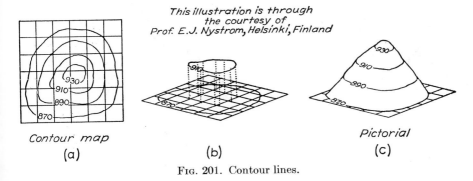

This illustration is through the courtesy of Prof. E.J. Nystrom, Helsinki, Finland

Contour map
(a)

(b)

Pictorial
(c)

FIG. 201. Contour lines.

149. BEARING OF A LINE

The bearing of a line is the method used to describe the *top* view of the line. It is entirely *independent* of the angle the line makes with *HRP*. All bearings of lines are based on the relationship of the *top* view of the lines with a north-south line which is conventionally vertical on the map, the direction north pointing to the top of the map. The angle of the bear-

ing may be considered as being the angle between
two planes perpendicular to *HRP*, with one plane
containing the north-south line and the other
plane containing the given line as shown in Fig.
202.   Line *AC* is said to have a bearing of N θ°
E.   Had the arrow of the *same* line been pointing
in the opposite direction, the bearing would have
been S θ° W.   Lines *AB*, *AD*, and *AE*, even
though they are not horizontal lines, have the
same bearing because they lie in the same vertical plane in which *AC* lies.   Lines *AF*, *AG*, *AH*,
and *AJ* all have the same bearing, which is S
θ° W.   The θ is always less than 90°.   Instead
of N 110° E, the correct bearing would be S
70° E.

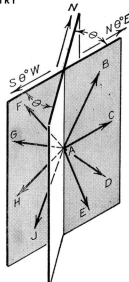

150. MINING AND GEOLOGICAL TERMINOLOGY   Fig. 202. Bearing of a line.

Problems involving mining and geological terminology may be more
readily understood if the technical terms are *translated* into their theoretical terms.   Figure 203 shows a table of the theoretical equivalents of
numerous technical terms.

Practical term	*Theoretical equivalent*
Dip	θ$_H$ or angle with *HRP*
Strike line	Horizontal line on a plane
Vein	Each side of vein represented by a plane
Hanging wall	Plane representing upper side of a vein
Foot wall	Plane representing lower side of a vein
Thickness of vein	Perpendicular distance between parallel sides of vein
Fault	A plane—representing a plane of slippage
Shaft	A line—to represent a vertical passage
Drill hole	A line—to represent a drilled hole
Tunnel	A line—to represent a passageway
Bearing	Direction of the *top* view of a line
Outcrop	Line of intersection of a plane with the earth's surface
Railway cut	A plane—representing a wall usually perpendicular to *HRP*
Contour line	Line of intersection of a horizontal plane at a specified elevation with the earth's surface
Cut	Surface formed by removal of earth
Fill	Surface formed by building up an area with dirt

Fig. 203. Translation of mining, geology, and civil engineering terminology to theoretical terminology.

151. ESTABLISHING THE DIP OF A VEIN

Three vertical holes are usually drilled in a triangular pattern at known elevations as indicated in Fig. 204 until the vein of ore is reached.   The depths of the vertical holes are scaled vertically from their respective contour elevations to establish the front view of the triangle which represents one side (the hanging wall) of the vein.

Since the dip of a vein is theoretically Θ_H, it is necessary to add the horizontal line BE to the plane.   Compare this method of determining dip with the method of determining Θ_H in Figs. 117 and 118.   As shown along the top view of BE, the bearing of the horizontal line is N 74° E, or it could rightfully be S 74° W.   The horizontal line is called a **strike line.** *Only* horizontal lines are called strike lines.

Either auxiliary view gives the dip (Θ_H) of the vein (plane).   The dip of a vein is shown in the top view by an arrow *perpendicular* to the strike line and pointing toward the *downward* side of the vein.   Point C is lower in elevation than the strike line BE.   The arrow points in the *general* direction of southeast; thus $\Theta°$ SE accompanies the arrow.

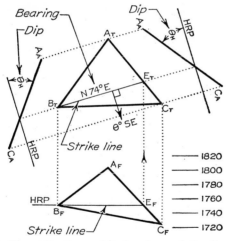

FIG. 204. The strike line and its bearing and the dip of a vein.

152. OUTCROP

Figure 205 shows a series of outcrop lines which are on the layers of rock cut by the vertical wall of the railroad.   Each outcrop line represents a line on one side of a layer of rock.   This does *not* mean that the planes of the sides of the layers of rock appear in their edge views; therefore the planes *cannot* be expected to have the same dip that these individual lines make with the horizontal.

FIG. 205. Outcrop lines on a vertical railroad cut.

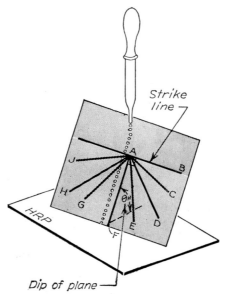

FIG. 206. Dip of lines on a vein.

The line AJ of the plane of Fig. 206 is comparable to the outcrop lines of Fig. 205.   The *only* line shown on the plane of Fig. 206 that indicates the *correct* slope of the plane is line AF, which, incidently, is perpendicular to the strike line.   The range of angles the individual lines of the plane of Fig. 206 make with HRP is from zero degrees for the strike line to $\Theta_H°$ for line AF.   Water falling on a plane will flow along the line having the *steepest* slope, in this case AF instead of any of the other lines because their angles with HRP are smaller.

The contour lines of Fig. 207 are shown in their edge views in the auxiliary view where the edge views of both sides of the vein also show.   The contour line 4320 intersects the edge views of both sides of the vein.

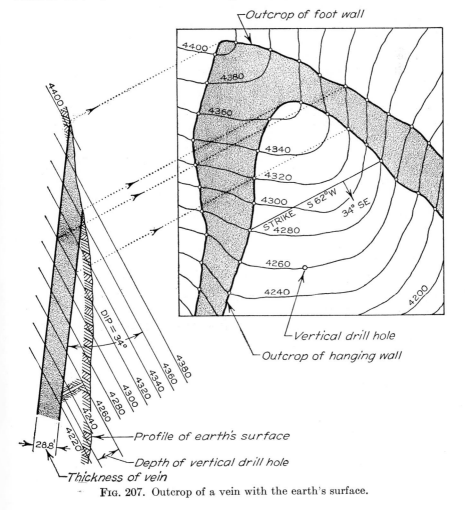

FIG. 207. Outcrop of a vein with the earth's surface.

These intersections were projected to the top view of contour line 4320 as points on the outcrop of the vein with the earth's surface. A vertical drill hole was drilled at 4260 elevation and is shown as such in the auxiliary view. The thickness of the vein is shown in the auxiliary view.

153. INTERSECTION OF TWO VEINS

The two strike lines A_TB_T and A_TM_T and the 35° SE and 45° SW dips of Fig. 208 were given. Since both strike lines are at the same elevation, they are in the same HRP and therefore they intersect at point A as one point on the line of intersection. Note that the points of each plane on the arrow side of the strike line are lower in elevation than their respective strike lines. Another strike line added to *each* plane at, say, 8840 elevation will intersect as did those at 8920 elevation. The point of intersection of these two 8840 strike lines at E is a second point on the line of intersection of these two veins. The strike line at 8880 elevation *cannot* intersect the 8840 strike line of the other plane, since they are in different HRPs.

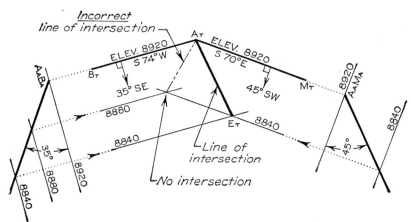

FIG. 208. Line of intersection of two mining veins.

154. CONTOUR LINES ON CUTS AND FILLS OF A ROADWAY

The slope of the cuts and fills of a roadway is constant whether the roadway is horizontal, inclined, straight, or curved. The usual amount of slope is shown in Fig. 209.

The cuts and fills are each tangent to a slope cone whose elements have the *same* slope as the cut and fill. This is comparable to the Θ_H (slope) cone of Fig. 175.

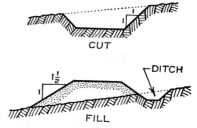

FIG. 209. Highway cross-sections.

The fill slope cone of Fig. 210 has its vertex at 5640 elevation on the edge of the roadway and is comparable to A_T of Fig. 175, while the edge of the roadway is comparable to the given line. The 5560 elevation is comparable to E_T. The base of the cone is also at 5560 elevation. Since the surface of the fill is a plane for a straight road, the contour line on the fill will be a straight line from 5560 on the roadway and tangent to the 5560 circle. Note the contour lines on the cone at various elevations. They are circles. The contour lines on the plane of the fill will be parallel straight lines. The slope cone for the cut is an inverted cone, but both fill and cut cones appear only as circles in the *top* view.

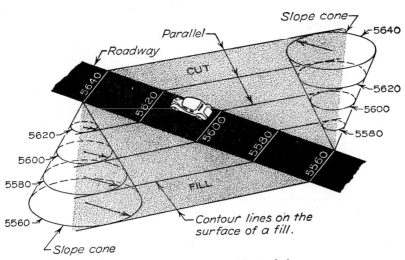

FIG. 210. Contour lines on cuts, fills, and slope cones.

Figure 211 shows a slope cone with the circles of the various elevations and the method of determining the slope as indicated. The unit 1 is *always* vertical. The radius of each circle is determined as indicated.

The contour line 4372 of Fig. 212 starts at 4372 elevation on the edge of the roadway. The vertex of a slope cone is placed at *each* contour line on the surface of the roadway. The radii of the arcs (it is *not* necessary to draw the full circles) are determined from a slope cone similar to Fig. 211. The elevations of the arcs should be labeled according to their elevations. In the left portion of Fig. 212 the roadway is straight; therefore the

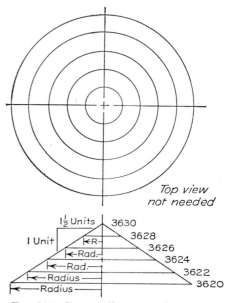

FIG. 211. Contour lines on a slope cone.

contour lines will be straight lines, and one contour line on the fill touches *all* the 4370 arcs. Another contour line will touch *all* the 4372 arcs. In the curved-road portion of the illustration the contour lines on the fill become curved lines.

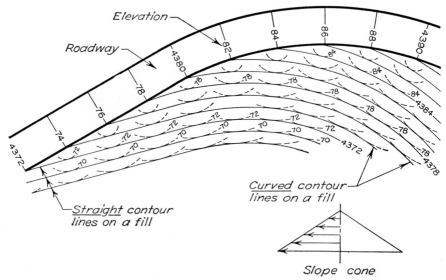

FIG. 212. Contour lines on a fill.

155. INTERSECTION OF CUTS AND FILLS WITH THE GROUND

Except for the upper left-hand corner of Fig. 213 where a cut exists, the inclined roadway and the parking area are fills. The vertices of the slope cones have been placed on the edge of the roadway and parking area. Since the parking area is horizontal, any convenient place for the slope cone is satisfactory. Since the corners of the parking area are rounded, the fills and cut will have their contour lines as true arcs of cones. The large arrows indicate the *downgrade* of the cut and fills. The cut arrow will point *toward* the parking area (or road), and the fill arrow away from the roadway and parking area.

A point on the intersection of the cut or fill with the ground is where a contour line at a particular elevation, say 664 of Fig. 213, on the fill intersects the contour line at 664 elevation on the ground. Follow the contour line of a cut or fill for its full length, and see where it intersects a contour line at the *same* elevation on the ground. The two contour lines may intersect at several places. As may be expected, the intersection of the fill of the parking area with that of the roadway is a straight line, since both fills are planes. Note how point B is found.

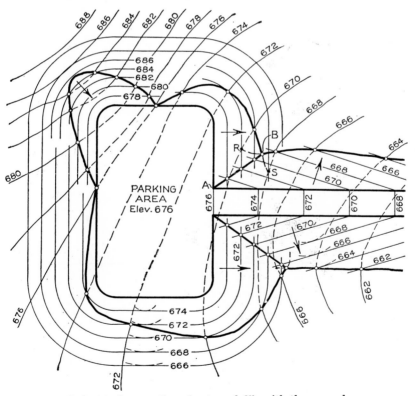

FIG. 213. Intersection of cuts and fills with the ground.

CHAPTER 12

SHADES AND SHADOWS

156. SHADES AND SHADOWS

This subject has been included in this text for three reasons. First, it is an excellent application of various fundamentals previously studied. Second, it offers a better understanding of photography, for shades and shadows affect the quality of a photograph. Third, it offers training in making us more observant of what is before us in our daily lives, for we "see" or "do not see" the beautiful effects of shades and shadows in direct relation to how observant we have trained ourselves to be. An interesting shadow is shown in Fig. 214.

FIG. 214. Shades and shadows.

The **shaded side** of an object is the portion of the object not receiving any direct sunlight at a given time.

The **shadow** is that portion of the surface of an object or the ground which does not receive light because of an intervening object or another portion of the same object.

The **shade line** is the line of separation between the lighted area and the shaded area of an object.

The **umbra** is the region in air between an object and its shadow that receives no sunlight.

157. SHADOWS CAST ON ONE PLANE

A line parallel to a plane will cast a shadow on the plane which is parallel to the line and of the same length as shown in Figs. 215a and b.   If the line is a curved line parallel to the plane, the cast shadow will likewise be the same.   Point A_S, which is the cast shadow of point A, is determined by drawing a line through A representing a ray of light piercing the plane.   The piercing point is determined by *any* method previously explained to determine the piercing point of a line with a plane.   A line through point B representing a ray of light will pierce the plane to locate the cast shadow B_S.   A line connecting A_S with B_S establishes the cast shadow of line AB.   In Fig. 215b only the center of the circle needs to be cast to the plane, since the cast shadow will be a circle.

In Fig. 215c the cast shadow of line AB on the plane is determined by finding the piercing points of a line through A and another through B, representing rays of light, with the horizontal plane.   Since AB and $A_S B_S$ lie in the same (umbra) plane, they will meet at C, which in numerous instances is a very useful point.

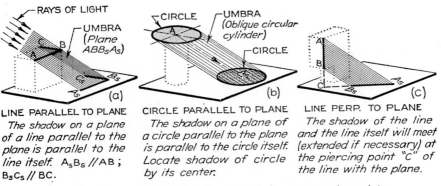

LINE PARALLEL TO PLANE   CIRCLE PARALLEL TO PLANE   LINE PERP. TO PLANE

The shadow on a plane   *The shadow on a plane of*   *The shadow of the line*
of a line parallel to the   *a circle parallel to the plane*   *and the line itself will meet*
plane is parallel to the   *is parallel to the circle itself.*   *(extended if necessary) at*
line itself. $A_S B_S$ // AB ;   *Locate shadow of circle*   *the piercing point "C" of*
$B_S C_S$ // BC.   *by its center.*   *the line with the plane.*

Shadow points A_S and B_S are found by finding the piercing points
of the rays of light through points A and B with the plane.

FIG. 215. Shadows of lines on a plane.

158. SHADOWS CAST ON PERPENDICULAR PLANES

Figure 216a shows line AB cast upon two perpendicular planes. This is a combination of Figs. 215a and c. $A_{S(\text{HORIZ})}$ and B_S may be located by the method previously explained. E_S, the bend point of the cast shadow, is at the intersection of both planes. $A_{S(\text{HORIZ})}$ is therefore only a theoretical shadow used to obtain E_S. $A_{S(\text{VERT})}$ may be determined by finding the piercing point of the line representing the ray of light through A with the vertical plane. E_S and $A_{S(\text{VERT})}$ of Fig. 216b may be similarly found.

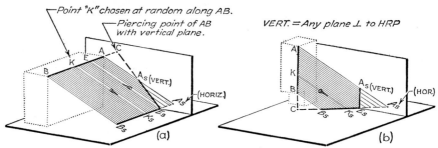

SHADOW OF LINE CAST UPON NON–PARALLEL PLANES
(GIVEN LINE PARALLEL TO ONE OF THE PLANES)

Point E_S may be found by connecting B_S and $A_{S(HORIZ)}$ or by extending $B_S K_S$. In part (a) point $A_{S(VERT)}$ may be found by connecting point "C" with E_S. In both (a) and (b) $A_{S(VERT)}$ may be found by finding where the ray of light through A pierces the vertical plane. Note: in part (a) $B_S E_S$ //AB ; in part (b) $A_{S(VERT)} E_S$ //AB.

FIG. 216. Shadows of normal lines on planes.

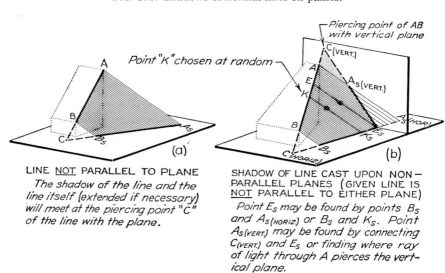

LINE <u>NOT</u> PARALLEL TO PLANE

The shadow of the line and the line itself (extended if necessary) will meet at the piercing point "C" of the line with the plane.

SHADOW OF LINE CAST UPON NON–PARALLEL PLANES (GIVEN LINE IS NOT PARALLEL TO EITHER PLANE)

Point E_S may be found by points B_S and $A_{S(HORIZ)}$ or B_S and K_S. Point $A_{S(VERT)}$ may be found by connecting $C_{(VERT)}$ and E_S or finding where ray of light through A pierces the vertical plane.

FIG. 217. Shadows of inclined and oblique lines on planes.

159. SHADOWS OF OBLIQUE LINES

In Fig. 217*a* lines representing rays of light through A and B will pierce the plane at A_s and B_s.   Since the umbra is a plane, AB and A_sB_s will intersect at C when they are extended.

In Fig. 217*b* either B_s and $A_{s(\text{HORIZ})}$ may be found or B_s and the cast shadow of *any* convenient point such as K.   Even though K_s is not the end of a line, it may be located in the *same* manner as any other point. B_sK_s extended to the intersection of the two planes locates E_s.   When the ray of light for E_s is *reversed*, point E on AB which casts the shadow may be found. AE will have its shadow cast on the vertical plane or wall.

160. SHADOWS CAST ON PARALLEL PLANES

In Fig. 218*a* A_sF_s and B_sG_s are parallel to AB and may be drawn after locating only A_s and $B_{s(1)}$. F_sG_s is the portion cast upon the riser.

In Fig. 218*b* point A_s may be connected with point C, which is in the *extension* of the plane of the top step 2. F_s may thus be located. $B_{s(1)}$ on step 1 may be located.   Care must be taken in orthographic views to get B_s on the correct step. $B_{s(2)}$ is on the *extension* of step 2 but is not on the step itself. G_s may be found by drawing through $B_{s(1)}$ the cast shadow on step 1 parallel to A_sC.   The umbra is a plane which intersects parallel planes (steps 1 and 2) in parallel lines. F_sG_s is the portion of the shadow cast on the riser.

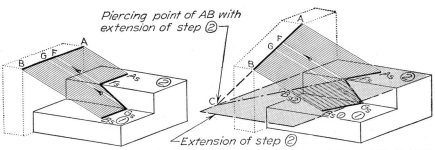

LINE PARALLEL TO PARALLEL PLANES
To find F_s and G_s locate A_s and B_s, then draw lines through them parallel to AB. FG is the portion of AB which has its shadow cast upon the riser.

LINE NOT PARALLEL TO PARALLEL PLANES
To find F_s locate A_s and from it draw a line to the piercing point "C" or $B_{s\,②}$ on the extension of step ②. To find G_s locate $B_{s①}$ and draw a line through it parallel to CA_s or $B_{s\,②}A_s$.

(a)   (b)

FIG. 218. Shadows of lines on parallel planes.

161. SHADOWS OF LINES CAST ON AN INCLINED PLANE

The shadow K_s of point K in Fig. 219a chosen at random and D_s will establish the shadow of BD on the horizontal plane. D_sK_s extended to the line of intersection of the two planes will locate E_s. B_s and A_s are usually more readily located in the edge view of the inclined plane. B_sA_s extended must include point C.

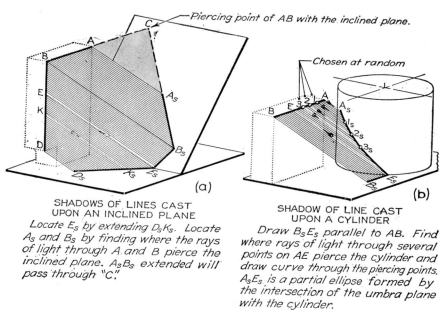

SHADOWS OF LINES CAST
UPON AN INCLINED PLANE
Locate E_s by extending D_sK_s. Locate
A_s and B_s by finding where the rays
of light through A and B pierce the
inclined plane. A_sB_s extended will
pass through "C".

SHADOW OF LINE CAST
UPON A CYLINDER
Draw B_sE_s parallel to AB. Find
where rays of light through several
points on AE pierce the cylinder and
draw curve through the piercing points.
A_sE_s is a partial ellipse formed by
the intersection of the umbra plane
with the cylinder.

FIG. 219. Shadows of lines on an inclined plane and a cylinder.

162. SHADOW OF A LINE CAST ON A CYLINDER

A series of points are chosen along the given line as shown in Fig. 219b. The piercing points of lines through these points with the cylinder are most readily found in the circular view of the cylinder. Since the umbra of a straight line is a plane, the shadow on the cylinder will usually be an ellipse. To find the shadow on *any* surface, find the piercing points of a number of the rays of light with the surface using *any* method convenient to use for finding the piercing point of a line with a plane or curved surface.

163. SHADOW OF A CONE CAST ON A PLANE

The two shade lines of the cone shown in Fig. 220a cast their shadows onto a plane in two lines which converge at the shadow of the vertex of the cone V_s and are tangent to the shadow of the base of the cone at the base ends of the shade lines. E_s of Fig. 220b is more readily determined by first finding $V_{s(\text{HORIZ})}$.

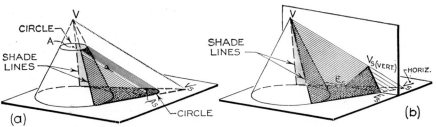

SHADOW OF A CONE ON A PLANE
Each shade line (along an element of cone) is the line of tangency of an umbra plane with the cone. There are two umbra planes tangent to the cone on opposite sides.

SHADOW OF A CONE ON NON—PARALLEL PLANES
In order to find the two E_S locate $V_{S (HORIZ.)}$ and then connect the two E_S with $V_{S (VERT.)}$. The shade side of the cone lies between the shade lines.

FIG. 220. Shades and shadows of cones.

164. SHADOW OF A CYLINDER CAST ON A PLANE

As shown in Fig. 221a, the shadows of the two shade lines are parallel and tangent to the shadow of each end of the cylinder. If the circles are parallel to the plane, their shadows will be circles.

When the plane in Fig. 221b is not parallel to the plane of the circle, the shadow of the circular end of the cylinder will invariably be an ellipse. The only exception occurs when the circle is parallel to the rays of light, and then a straight line would be the shadow. A series of points on one-half of the circle between the ends of shade lines are chosen. Lines

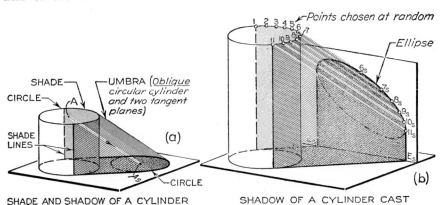

SHADE AND SHADOW OF A CYLINDER
The shadows of the shade lines will be parallel and tangent to the base of the cylinder. The shadow of the upper base will be a circle when the circle and plane are parallel.

SHADOW OF A CYLINDER CAST UPON NON—PARALLEL PLANES
The two E_S are found by drawing the shadows of the shade lines. The ellipse is the intersection of the umbra (oblique circ. cyl.) with the plane. To locate points on the ellipse find where the rays of light through points on circle of the cylinder pierce the plane.

FIG. 221. Shades and shadows of cylinders.

representing rays of light through these points pierce the plane to create the shadow of that half of the circular end. Points 1 and 11 establish the tangency points on the shadow of the ellipse with the straight lines.

165. SHADOW OF A SPHERE CAST ON A PLANE

The shade line of the sphere shown in Fig. 222a will *always* be a circle and always *perpendicular* to the rays of light. This makes the umbra a right circular cylinder. The shadow is theoretically the intersection of the umbra with the plane, which invariably will be an ellipse. For ease of establishing this shadow, first find the true lengths of the rays of light in an auxiliary view. The remainder will be readily understood. Notice the cast shadow of a spherical street-lamp globe.

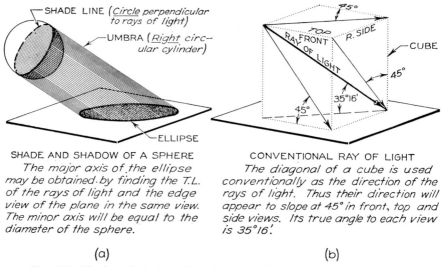

SHADE AND SHADOW OF A SPHERE
The major axis of the ellipse may be obtained by finding the T.L. of the rays of light and the edge view of the plane in the same view. The minor axis will be equal to the diameter of the sphere.

CONVENTIONAL RAY OF LIGHT
The diagonal of a cube is used conventionally as the direction of the rays of light. Thus their direction will appear to slope at 45° in front, top and side views. Its true angle to each view is 35°16'.

(a)   (b)

FIG. 222. Shade and shadow of a sphere and the conventional ray of light.

166. RAY OF LIGHT

At different times of the day as well as of the year the rays of light slope in different directions. They all converge at the sun.

For the purposes of simplicity all the rays of light shall be considered parallel and their top, front, and side views shall be considered to slope at 45° as shown in Fig. 222b. The rays of light shall be assumed to be coming from the upper left, front position. Note the direction of arrows in each of the three regular views. The ray of light that will appear to slope at 45° in each of the three regular views actually makes 35°16' with HRP. This will show only when the rays of light are true length in an auxiliary view.

167. SHADOWS OF OBJECTS

The rays of light through the corners of the object of Fig. 223a slope in the front and top views at 45°. The rays of light through corners A, B, and C pierce the vertical wall at A_S, B_S, and C_S *before* they reach the floor (HRP). The ray of light through corner O pierces the floor at O_S *before* it pierces the vertical wall. Part of the shadow of edge CO is cast on the floor, and the remainder on the wall (see Fig. 216b). Since CO is parallel to the wall, the portion of the shadow of CO on the wall will be vertical. The vertical shadow line through C_S meets the line of intersection of the wall with the floor at F_S. By this means, F_S, which is the *bend* point of the shadow of CO, is found. Bend point E_S is similarly determined. Take each edge of the object and compare its shadow with Figs. 215 and 216, where each one is shown individually.

Figure 223b has an inclined surface $V_T Q_T W_T$ appearing in its edge view in the top view, and surface $YVWR$ appears in its edge view in the side view. Edge VW is oblique. With the exception of the normal edges, the

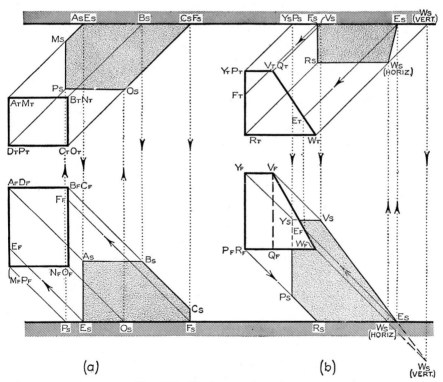

FIG. 223. Shadows on two planes.

oblique edge is the only edge of the object in Fig. 223*b* which affects the outline of the shadow.

The shadow of the oblique line VW should be compared with Fig. 217*b*. The ray of light through V pierces the vertical wall *before* it reaches the floor, while the ray of light through W pierces the floor *before* it reaches the vertical wall. Thus edge VW casts its shadow on both planes and has a bend point at E_S. Temporarily ignore the floor and note that the shadow of VW on the vertical wall is $V_sW_{s(\text{VERT})}$. This shadow intersects the floor and locates E_S in the front view. It may then be projected to the top view, where it will connect with $W_{s(\text{HORIZ})}$.

168. SHADOW OF A SPHERE CAST ON A PLANE

The rays of light should first be found true length in an auxiliary view as shown in Fig. 224. In this view the floor appears in its edge view and the shade line also appears in its edge view. The other views of the shade line may be established from this edge view.

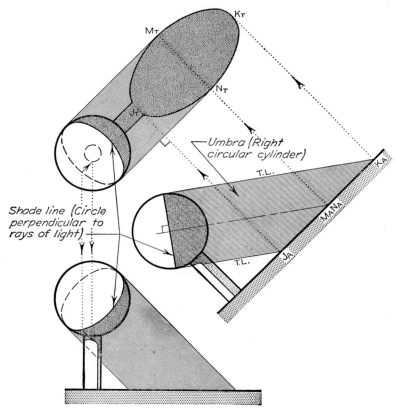

Fig. 224. Shade and shadow of a sphere on a plane.

The minor axis of the ellipse shadow of the sphere appears in its point view at $M_A N_A$, and the true length of the major axis is $J_A K_A$. The ellipse may be drawn in the top view by the trammel or concentric-circle method.

Several rays of light may be taken through points on the top view of the shade line for the purpose of locating the shadow of the sphere on the cylindrical pedestal. Their piercing points with the cylinder may be determined in the top view and then projected to the front view.

CHAPTER 13

CURVED SURFACES

169. CURVED-SURFACE DEFINITIONS

Curved surfaces may be divided into ruled and double-curved surfaces.

A **ruled surface** is a surface which is generated by a straight line. The ruled surfaces may be divided into single-curved and warped surfaces.

A **single-curved surface** is a *ruled* surface that can be developed, that is, rolled into a plane.

A **warped surface** is a *ruled* surface that *cannot* be developed.

A **double-curved surface** is a surface which is generated by *only* a curved line. Most of these surfaces are surfaces of revolution.

A **surface of revolution** is a surface generated by revolving a *straight* or *curved* line about an axis. Most of the curved lines are known curves such as circles, ellipses, parabolas, and hyperbolas.

Warped and double-curved surfaces are pressed into shape by forming dies (for automobile bodies, fenders, etc.) or by being cast in a mold or by being shaped with cutting tools or by hand. The curved surfaces are classified in the table in Fig. 225.

170. RULED SURFACES

Cones and cylinders, although they are ruled surfaces, have been explained in Chapter 9.

The **convolute** is a *ruled* surface which is generated by a straight line tangent to a helix. See Arts. 208 to 212 for information on a helix.

The convolute is more readily drawn first in the circular view of the helix and cylinder. The straight lines will appear tangent to the circle as shown in Fig. 226. With the base of the convolute perpendicular to the axis of the helix, the foreshortened lengths of the straight lines in the circular view (top view in Fig. 226) will be equal to the length of the arc from zero to the tangency point. For example, 3-3 in the top view is equal to the length of the arc from 0 to 3. Draw a line tangent to the circle through 3 on the circle, and measure the arc length 0-3, thereby

				Developable
Ruled	Single-curved (Developable)	Surfaces of revolution	Cone	Yes
			Cylinder	Yes
		Cone		Yes
		Cylinder		Yes
		Convolute		Yes
	Warped (Not developable)	Surface of revolution	Hyperboloid of revolution of one sheet	No
		Conoid		No
		Cow's horn		No
		Warped cone		No
		Cylindroid		No
		Helicoid		No
		Hyperbolic paraboloid		No
Double-curved	Surface of revolution	Sphere		No
		Torus		No
		Oblate ellipsoid		No
		Prolate ellipsoid		No
		Hyperboloid of revolution of two sheets		No
		Paraboloid		No
	Irregular	Serpentine		No
		Unnamed		No

Fig. 225. Tabulation of curved surfaces.

allowing the tangent line to locate 3 on the base. One end of this tangent line is on the front view of the helix, and the other on the edge view of the base. The straightline element 7-7 is true length in the front view. Its angle with the base is the helix angle of the helix itself. All tangent lines (elements) make the *same* angle with the base.

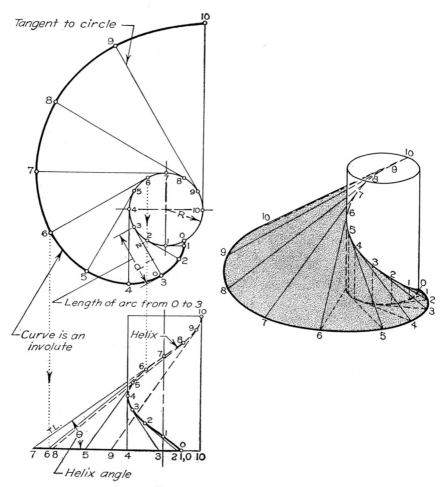

FIG. 226. The convolute.

An application of a convolute is the surface of the face of a helical involute gear tooth.* Figure 227 shows one tooth. The involute curve of Fig. 226 is the shape of the end of the tooth and the straight lines of the surface are tangent to the helix.

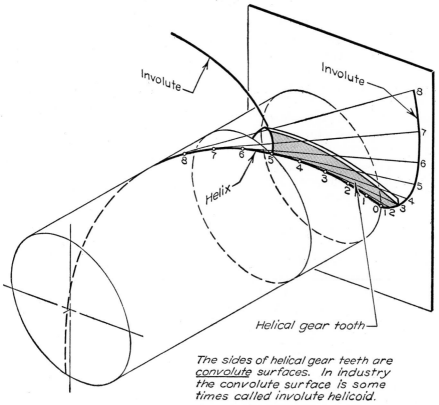

The sides of helical gear teeth are convolute surfaces. In industry the convolute surface is some times called involute helicoid.

Fig. 227. Application of the convolute.

171. WARPED SURFACES

Adjacent positions of the generating line of a warped surface are skewed lines; therefore warped surfaces are *not* developable. Even though these surfaces are not developable, they are very useful surfaces in industry as the several following illustrations indicate.

* For further information about the convolute surface of helical gear teeth see "Equations for the Normal Profile of Helical Gears" by Anthony F. Zamis in the Sept. 25, 1947, issue of *American Machinist*.

172. HYPERBOLOID OF REVOLUTION OF ONE SHEET

A **hyperboloid of revolution** is a *warped* surface generated by revolving one skew line about the other as shown in Fig. 131. It also may be generated by revolving a hyperbola about one of its two axes of symmetry.

Figure 228 shows a skew line *A*-1 revolved about an axis. Twenty-four equidistant positions of the generating line *A*-1 are shown. They are all tangent to the gorge circle, which may be drawn tangent to the original line *A*-1. The true length and point views of the axis are essential in order to draw this surface. The outline of the front view of Fig. 228 is a hyperbola.

Figure 229 shows an application of this surface. Pipes, tubing, and rods are bent in shipping and are straightened by a series of hyperboloids of revolution. The rod touches one straight-line element of each hyperboloid of revolution.

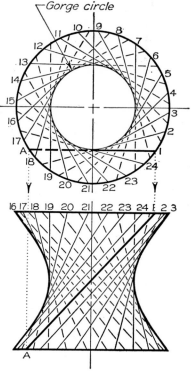

Fig. 228. The hyperboloid of revolution of one sheet.

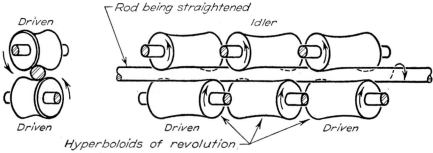

Fig. 229. Application of the hyperboloid of revolution.

Hyperboloids of revolution are also used on centerless grinding machines. They will advance the work through the machine, while cylinders will not.

When lathe centers are offset *vertically* as shown in Fig. 230, a hyperboloid of revolution will be produced. This surface may be cut on a planer if the axis of revolution is not parallel to the longitudinal direction of the table.

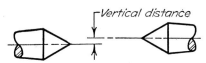

Lathe centers offset vertically, intentionally or not, will produce a hyperboloid of revolution.

FIG. 230. One method of machining a hyperboloid of revolution.

FIG. 231. (*Right*) Hypoid gears and their hyperboloids of revolution. (*Courtesy of Prof. E. J. Nystrom, Technical University, Helsinki, Finland.*)

Figure 231 shows a model of the two rolling hyperboloids of revolution in a pair of hypoid gears used in today's automobiles and other equipment.* The two hyperboloids have one straight line of contact. The single straight-line contact is line *AB* of Fig. 232. The edge of each gear tooth is a straight-line element of a hyperboloid of revolution. The bases of the hyperboloids of revolution (gears) are determined in the view where both axes appear true length. Both bases will appear in their edge views through the ends of the line of contact which must be on *both* surfaces.

* For additional information on the hyperboloids of revolution of hypoid gears see "Basic Relationship of Hypoid Gears" by Ernest Wildhaber in the Feb. 14, 1946, issue of *American Machinist.*

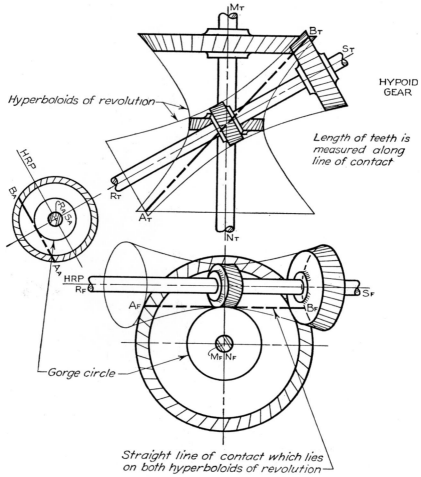

FIG. 232. Hypoid gears and their hyperboloids of revolution.

173. RIGHT HELICOID

A **right helicoid** is a *warped* surface generated by a straight line touching a helix and is perpendicular to the axis of the helix. Although in most applications the generating line intersects the axis of the helix, the definition does *not* require it.

Figure 233 shows several applications of the right helicoid on threads and a spring. Other applications are screw conveyors and fan and propeller blades.

Figure 234 shows pictorially a right helicoid with the helix on a cylinder. The generating line appears in a radial position in the point view of the axis. The circular view of the helix is divided into twelve equal parts.

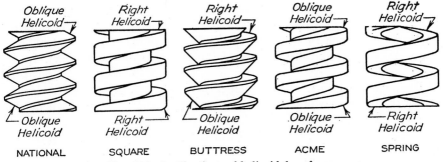

FIG. 233. Applications of helicoidal surfaces.

The lead, which is the distance along the axis from 1 (near top of axis) to 1 (near bottom of axis), is also divided into twelve equal parts.   The

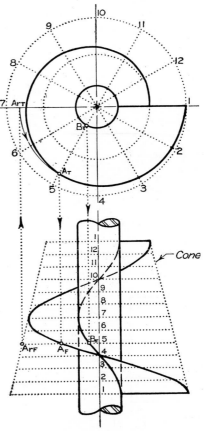

length of the projection from 5 on the circle, through point 1, to 5 on the helix is the same as from 1 to 5 on the axis.

A right helicoid with a conical outline is shown in Fig. 235.   The base of the cone is divided into twelve equal parts, and the lead (in this example it is the height of the front view) is also divided into twelve equal parts.   The helix is

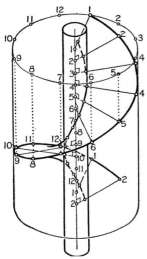

FIG. 234. A right helicoid.

FIG. 235. A right helicoid with a conical outline.

drawn on the cone as explained in Art. 211 and on the cylinder as explained in Art. 209. Point A on the helix of the cone is determined by considering A_F as having been revolved to the FRP containing the axis which will place A_{rF} on the contour element of the cone as shown. Project A_{rF} to the top view to A_{rT}, and then revolve A_{rT} to A_T on the No. 5 position of the generating line. A_T is then projected to the front view to locate A_F on the front view of the generating line through 5. Point B_T is on the circular view of the cylinder and on the No. 5 position of the generating line; therefore it may be projected to the front view without any previous revolution.

The conical outlined right helicoid is used in concrete mixers.

174. FAN AND PROPELLER BLADES

Fan and propeller blades are either right or oblique helicoids, depending upon the job requirements.

Figure 236 is a drawing of one blade. Since fan and propeller blades are specified on the basis of their helix angles, the development of the

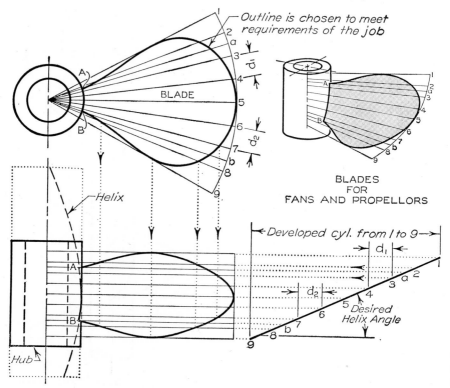

FIG. 236. Application of a right helicoid.

helix is required. The helix is developed by computing the true length of the arc from 1 to 9 in the top view and using it as shown in Fig. 236. Computing is more accurate than using several chord measurements. The helix in this developed view will appear as a straight line and therefore may be drawn at the desired helix angle. The helix is then divided into eight (not nine) equal spaces. Points a and b are located by chord measurements similar to d_1 and d_2. The developed view of the cylinder will give the elevation in the front view for each position of the generated line from 1 to 9. The outline of the blade in the top view intersects the several positions of the generating line. The points of intersection when projected onto the front view of the respective lines give the necessary points for drawing the front view of the blade.

175. RIGHT HELICOID (Generating Line Not Intersecting the Axis)

In Fig. 237 the generating line AB is perpendicular to the axis but does *not* intersect it. Point C is the closest point of the generating line to the axis. The circular view is divided into sixteen equal angular parts, and the lead into sixteen equal parts. The ends of each position of the generating line in the circular view are projected to the front view of the generating line.

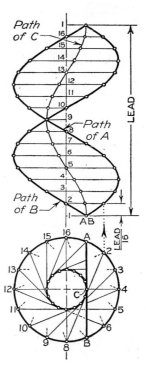

Fig. 237. A right helicoid with the generating line not intersecting the axis.

Figure 238 shows a pictorial and an application of this type of helicoid. This application requires a constant cross section. A rectangular iron bar when twisted also forms this surface.

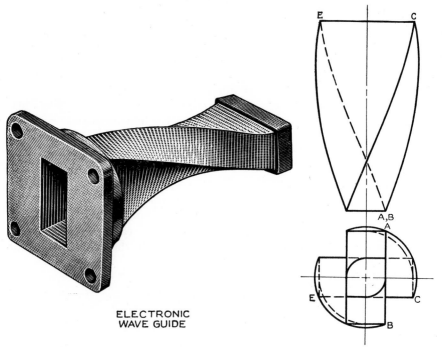

ELECTRONIC
WAVE GUIDE

FIG. 238. Application of the right helicoid with the generating line not intersecting the axis.

176. OBLIQUE HELICOID

Several thread applications of oblique helicoids are shown in Fig. 233.

In an **oblique helicoid** the generating line maintains a fixed angle with the axis. This angle will appear in its true size *only* when the axis and the generating line are *both* true length in the same view.

In Fig. 239 the circular view is divided into sixteen equal parts. The lead is from 1 to 1 along the axis, and this likewise is divided into sixteen equal parts. The generating line 1-1 as well as the axis are true length in the front view. The angle of the generating line with the axis is measured as indicated. Point 1 on the helix is the starting point. Point 1 on the axis is determined by measuring the true angle of the helicoid. The lead is then measured from point 1 on the axis. With the base of the helicoid drawn perpendicular to the axis through point 1 on the helix, the base may be used to locate points of the helix. Measurement d measured from 1 to 8 on the axis may be used to locate point 8 on the

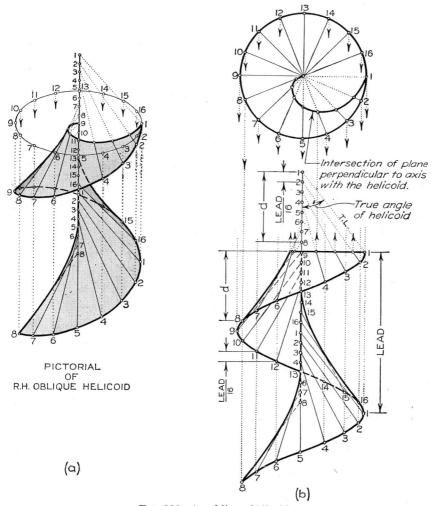

PICTORIAL
OF
R.H. OBLIQUE HELICOID

(a)

Intersection of plane
perpendicular to axis
with the helicoid.

True angle
of helicoid

(b)

FIG. 239. An oblique helicoid.

helix.   Project point 8 from the top view to the front view, and locate 8 in the front view by measuring the measurement d from the base.   All other points are similarly located.

Figure 240 is an application of an oblique helicoid between cones except the bottom, which is a partial torus.   The angle of the helicoid is 45°. Since the beginning point R_F of the two helices at the top of the front view is on the same FRP as the axis, the generating line will be true length and the angle true size.   Thus point 1 on the axis may be located.   The

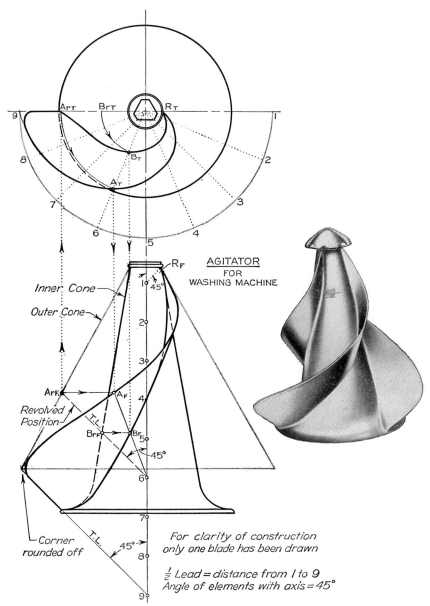

AGITATOR
FOR
WASHING MACHINE

Inner Cone

Outer Cone

A_{TF}

Revolved
Position

Corner
rounded off

*For clarity of construction
only one blade has been drawn*

$\frac{1}{2}$ *Lead = distance from 1 to 9*
Angle of elements with axis = 45°

*Draw T.L. of each element of the surface, find where
each pierces both cones then rotate the elements and
piercing points to their space positions.*

Fig. 240. Application of an oblique helicoid.

distance on the axis from 1 to 9 is one-half the lead.   One-half of the top
view is divided into eight parts from 1 to 9 in the same manner in which
the one-half lead is divided into eight equal parts.

The No. 6 position of the generating line locates points A and B.
Draw through No. 6 on the axis the true-length *revolved* No. 6 position of
the generating line at 45° to the axis.   This line in its revolved position
will intersect the contour elements of both cones at A_{rF} and B_{rF}.   Project
A_{rF} and B_{rF} to the top view; then revolve them to the top view of No. 6
position of the generating line. A_T and B_T may then be projected to the
front view to locate A_F and B_F.   Other points on the helices are similarly
located.

177. HYPERBOLIC PARABOLOID

The **hyperbolic paraboloid** is a *warped* surface generated by a line
touching two skew lines and remaining parallel to a plane not parallel
to either line.

In Fig. 241a the skew lines are AB and CE, and HRP is the plane

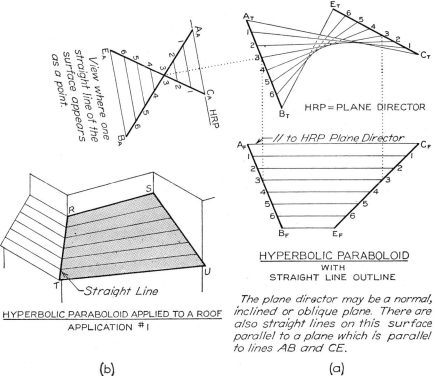

HRP = PLANE DIRECTOR

HYPERBOLIC PARABOLOID
WITH
STRAIGHT LINE OUTLINE

HYPERBOLIC PARABOLOID APPLIED TO A ROOF
APPLICATION #1

*The plane director may be a normal,
inclined or oblique plane. There are
also straight lines on this surface
parallel to a plane which is parallel
to lines AB and CE.*

(b)   (a)

Fig. 241. Hyperbolic paraboloid and its application.

director to which the generating line remains parallel. Since all generating lines are parallel to HRP, they are true length in the top view. The auxiliary view shows the point view of one position of the generating line.

Figure 241b is an application of this surface where RT and SU are the skew lines and the generating line is again parallel to HRP.

Figure 242 shows another roof application of this surface. AB and SU are the skew lines, and the generating line is parallel to HRP. This surface intersects an inclined roof surface to form the curved line R_TT_T.

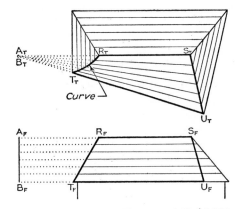

HYPERBOLIC PARABOLOID APPLIED TO A ROOF

APPLICATION #2

FIG. 242. Application of a hyperbolic paraboloid.

In its theoretical form the hyperbolic paraboloid is represented in numerous texts in various outlines and from various directions. Figure 243 shows one of these shapes. The parabola and hyperbola sections are labeled. Although this surface does not appear to have the remotest similarity to Figs. 241 and 242, it is nevertheless the *same* surface.

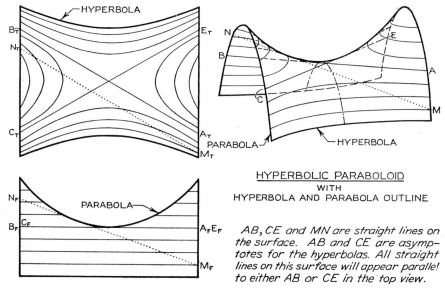

HYPERBOLIC PARABOLOID
WITH
HYPERBOLA AND PARABOLA OUTLINE

AB, CE and MN are straight lines on the surface. AB and CE are asymptotes for the hyperbolas. All straight lines on this surface will appear parallel to either AB or CE in the top view.

FIG. 243. Hyperbolic paraboloid.

178. CONOID

A **conoid** is a *warped* surface generated by moving a straight line in such a manner that it is always parallel to a plane and always touches a *straight* line and a *curved* line. If the curved line is a circle, the conoid is a circular conoid. In a right conoid the given line is perpendicular to the plane director. Figure 244a shows a right circular conoid.

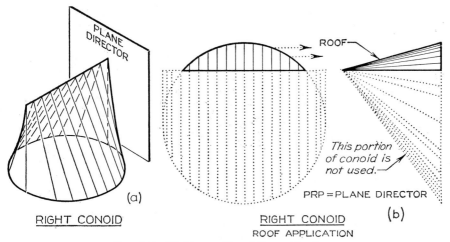

Fig. 244. Right conoid and its application.

Figure 244b is a drawing of a roof application of a conoid. Figures 245a and b show roofs in two stages of construction, and Fig. 245c shows a completed roof. Although this surface is theoretically undevelopable, it can be closely approximated by the relatively narrow boards and sheet metal. Compare the construction with the drawing, line for line, and note the curvature of the surface.

Fig. 245. Application of a right conoid.

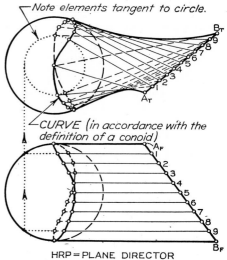

Figure 246 is an oblique conoid tangent to a sphere. The line of tangency is the *curved* line of the definition. The generating line in each of its positions is tangent to a circle of the sphere lying in a plane parallel to the plane director and contains a given position of the generating line.

FIG. 246. Oblique conoid tangent to a sphere.

179. CYLINDROID

A **cylindroid** is a *warped* surface generated by a straight line moving parallel to a plane and touching two curved lines.

In Fig. 247 the generating line is parallel to *HRP* and touches the two curved lines *AB* and *CE* to form the archway between two doorways.

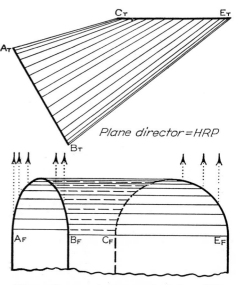

Elements are drawn parallel to HRP then projected to the top view

ARCHWAY CONNECTING NON-PARALLEL DOORWAYS

FIG. 247. Cylindroid.

180. WARPED CONE

A **warped cone** is a *warped* surface generated by a line touching two curved lines and a straight line. In practice the straight line usually connects the centers of the curved lines (usually circles or ellipses).

In Fig. 248 the straight-line directrix of the definition connects the centers of the two semicircles AB and CE and appears as a point in the front view. Draw the various positions (elements) of the generating line in the front view through the point view of the straight-line directrix *before* drawing them in the top view. This assures that the generating line touches all required lines. Project to the top view the points of

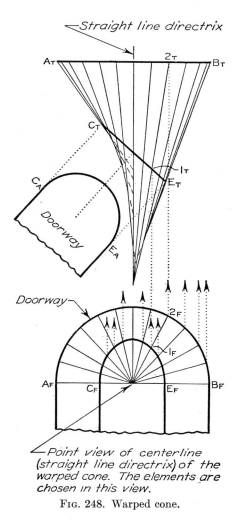

Fig. 248. Warped cone.

intersection, such as 1_F and 2_F, of the generating line with the two curved lines. The extension of the generating line through the top view 1_T and 2_T of these two points will intersect the top view of the straight-line directrix.

181. COW'S HORN

The **cow's horn** is the second *warped* surface generated by a straight line touching two curved lines and a straight line. In practice the straight-line directrix usually connects the centers of the two curved lines, which are usually in parallel planes.

In Fig. 249 the two curved lines are AB and CE. The straight-line directrix appears in its point view in the front view from which all positions of the generating line appear to radiate. The points, such as 1_F and 2_F, where the various positions of the generating line intersect the two curves in the front view are projected to the corresponding curves in the top view. The line 1_T2_T extended would intersect the extension of the straight-line directrix. The MN position of the generating line is parallel to the straight-line directrix. The positions of the generating line to the right of MN intersect the *opposite* end of the straight-line directrix. In other words, note where the AC and BE positions of the generating line, when extended, intersect the straight-line directrix.

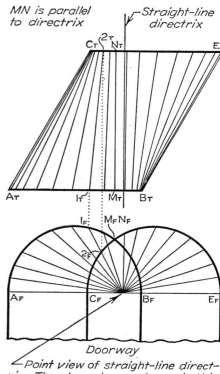

FIG. 249. Cow's horn.

182. DOUBLE-CURVED SURFACES AND SURFACES OF REVOLUTION

Since **double-curved** surfaces are formed by generating a *curved* line, there are *no* straight lines on the surfaces. In most practical applications the curved line is generated about a straight line as an axis of revolution.

Figure 250 shows several double-curved surfaces of revolution. Figure 251 shows three applications of double-curved surfaces of revolution.

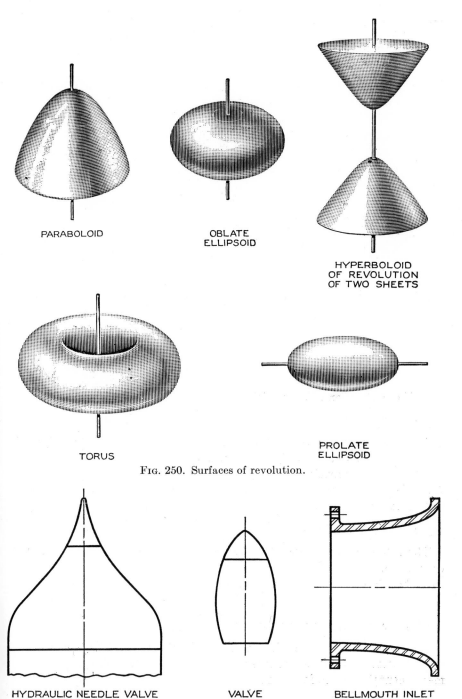

PARABOLOID

OBLATE
ELLIPSOID

HYPERBOLOID
OF REVOLUTION
OF TWO SHEETS

TORUS

PROLATE
ELLIPSOID

Fig. 250. Surfaces of revolution.

HYDRAULIC NEEDLE VALVE

VALVE

BELLMOUTH INLET

Fig. 251. Application of surfaces of revolution.

183. PARABOLOIDS

Figure 252 is a paraboloid which is created by revolving a parabola about its axis of symmetry.   With the source of light at the focal point, the rays of light will be reflected parallel to the axis.   Automobile head-lamp reflectors and some home reading lamps are paraboloids.   Television reflectors are also paraboloids, although they are very flat, that is, of the saucer type.   Several light reflectors use a combination of sphere and paraboloid.

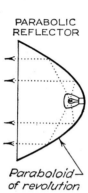

PARABOLIC
REFLECTOR

Paraboloid
of revolution

FOCAL POINT

PROLATE
ELLIPSOID
(*For theatre*
"pin-spot"
lighting)

FOCAL POINT

FIG. 252. Application of a paraboloid.   FIG. 253. Application of prolate ellipsoid.

184. ELLIPSOIDS

An ellipse revolved about its major axis generates a **prolate ellipsoid.** An ellipse revolved about its minor axis generates an **oblate ellipsoid.**

The prolate ellipsoid is used as a reflector for lighting (see Fig. 253). A number of reflectors use a combination of sphere, ellipsoid, and parabo-loid surfaces.

185. SPHERE AND TORUS

The **sphere** and **torus** are *double-curved* surfaces of revolution generated by revolving a circle about an axis.   The center of the circle generating the sphere is on the axis, while the center of the circle generating the torus is off the axis.

186. HYPERBOLOID OF REVOLUTION OF TWO SHEETS

The **hyperboloid of revolution of two sheets** is a *double-curved* surface of revolution generated by revolving a hyperbola about the axis of sym-metry containing the focal points.

CHAPTER 14

PLANE AND CURVED SURFACE INTERSECTIONS

187. CHANGING PRACTICAL INTERSECTION PROBLEMS TO THEORETICAL PROBLEMS

In practice the cylinders, cones, spheres, toruses, etc., are *not* the full surfaces generated by straight or curved lines. Instead, only a small portion of the surface is actually used in numerous instances. The *full shape* of the surface should be drawn in the *constructive* stage before attempting to solve the problem.

Figure 254*a* shows the complete right circular cone and the small por-

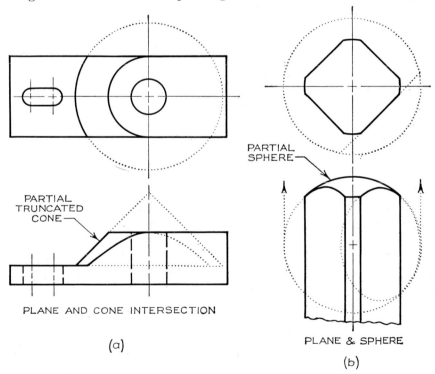

PARTIAL SPHERE

PARTIAL TRUNCATED CONE

PLANE AND CONE INTERSECTION

(a)

PLANE & SPHERE

(b)

Fig. 254. Changing practical problems to theoretical problems.

tion actually used on the object. The solution of the problem is more readily visualized when the *whole* cone is drawn in the constructive stage.

Figure 254*b* shows the completed sphere and the small portion the object requires. It is a good practice *always* to draw the *complete* geometrical object *before* starting to solve the practical problem.

188. PLANE AND CYLINDER INTERSECTION

Figure 255*a* shows two methods of determining points on the curve of intersection of the plane with the cylinder. The intersection of a plane and a circular cylinder will always be an ellipse, circle, or two straight lines.

In the edge view of the plane intersecting the cylinder in the auxiliary view, straight-line elements are taken at *random* on the surface of the cylinder and then projected to the top and front views. The two elements 1 and 2 of the cylinder pierce the edge view of the plane at *A* and *B*. *A* and *B* are then projected to the top and front views of the elements on which they lie. A series of these elements is taken but so spaced that the points *on the curve* itself are *approximately evenly* spaced.

The second method uses a cutting plane perpendicular to a reference plane and parallel to the elements of the cylinder. Such a cutting plane appears in its edge view in the top view. It cuts the straight line *JK* on the given plane and two elements 7 and 8 on the cylinder. The two

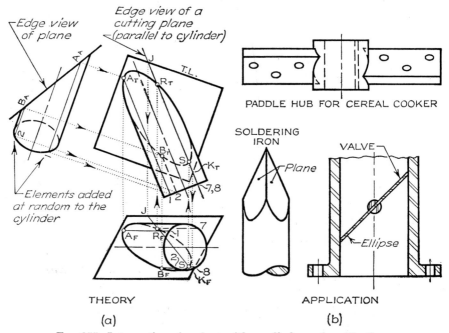

THEORY

(a)

APPLICATION

(b)

FIG. 255. Intersection of a plane with a cylinder and applications.

elements 7 and 8 intersect the line JK in the front view to create two
points R and S on the curve of intersection.   It is *not* necessary that the
cutting plane be taken in its edge view parallel to the true length of the
center line (axis) of the cylinder.   As the contour elements are approached,
the cutting planes should be taken closer together; otherwise the points
on the curve of intersection will be farther apart.   The cutting planes
should *not* be taken at equidistant intervals because they do *not* cut elements on the cylinder at equidistant intervals.   Figure 255b shows three
applications of this intersection.

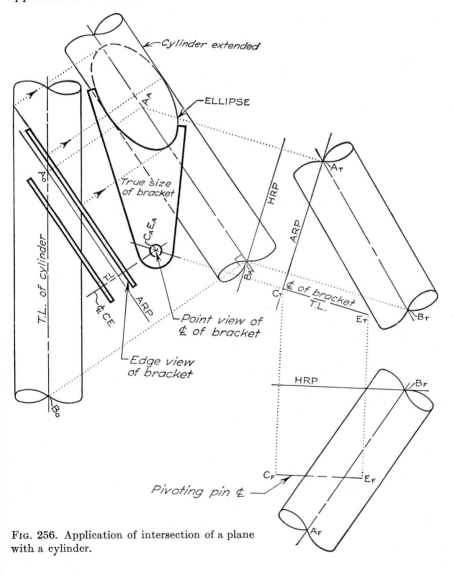

Fig. 256. Application of intersection of a plane
with a cylinder.

Figure 256 is another type of practical application of plane and cylinder intersection. The problem is to construct a bracket with its pivoting pin center line *CE* oblique to the cylinder. The sides of the bracket are to be of plate stock and cut to conform to their intersection with the cylinder. In solving for this bracket the *point* view of the center line *CE* and its *true length* view will give the edge view and the true size view of the plate stock (consider it a plane). The point view of the center line *CE* is determined in the primary auxiliary view. *Any* auxiliary view taken from this auxiliary view will again show the true length of the center line *CE*. But if the line of sight for this secondary auxiliary view is taken perpendicular to the center line of the cylinder, the center line of the cylinder as well as that of *CE* will show true length. The edge view of each side of the bracket is perpendicular to the center line *CE*. The major and minor axes of the ellipse intersection are determined as shown. See Fig. 328 for more information about the axes of the ellipse. The bracket is shaped to conform to the intersection of the plate stock (plane) with the cylinder.

189. PLANE AND CONE INTERSECTION

Figure 257*a* shows two methods of finding the line of intersection of a plane with a cone. The various curves of intersection thus determined are explained in Chap. 10 and are illustrated pictorially in Fig. 184.

The edge view of the plane intersecting the cone is shown in the auxiliary view. Elements such as 1 and 2 are added to the cone, and they pierce the plane at points *A* and *B*. The elements and the piercing points are projected from view to view. The piercing points are on the curve of intersection. Elements are *not* equally spaced in the auxiliary view but may be equally spaced in the circular view of the cone.

The second method uses a series of cutting planes which are either parallel to the circular base of the cone or contain the center line (axis) of the cone. A cutting plane parallel to the base of the cone appears in its edge view in the front view. This cutting plane intersects the given plane in line 7-8 and a circle on the cone. The intersection of the cutting plane and the contour elements of the cone gives the diameter of the circle. The circle and the line 7-8 intersect in the true-size view (top view) of the circle to create the two points *R* and *S* on the curve of intersection. A series of cutting planes gives additional points on the curve of intersection.

The cutting planes could also have been taken in the point view of the center line of the cone (top view in Fig. 257*a*). They would then appear in their edge views and contain the point view of the center line. Thus the edge views of the cutting planes would appear as radial lines with the point view of the center line as a common point. *Each* cutting plane would cut two straight-line elements on the cone and one line on the given plane which would intersect to create two points on the curve of intersection.

Figure 257*b* shows three applications of the intersection of a plane with a cone.

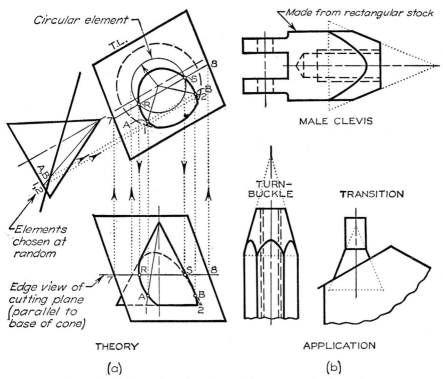

FIG. 257. Intersection of a plane with a cone and applications.

190. PLANE AND TORUS INTERSECTION

Figure 258 is an example of a *partial* torus. The completed torus is shown in fine lines. Cutting planes perpendicular to the axis of the torus cut circles on the torus. The circles appear true size in the top view where they pierce the edge view of the intersecting plane. The circles may be chosen first in the top view, which is the point view of the axis of the torus. Circle 1 was chosen tangent to the edge view of the intersecting plane. The front view of the edge view of this circle (which is also the edge view of the cutting plane that created the circle) is determined by projecting the extremities of the circle to the front view and onto the outline of the torus. The edge view of the circle, of course, must be perpendicular to the axis. The tangency point of circle 1 with the edge view of the intersecting plane in the top view locates the *highest* point on this portion of the curve of intersection. Circle 2 *pierces* the edge view of the plane at *B* and *C* and will be on the edge view of the circle in the front view. The entire curve of intersection is shown.

In Fig. 259 the edge view of the intersecting plane is in the auxiliary view. Note the exten-

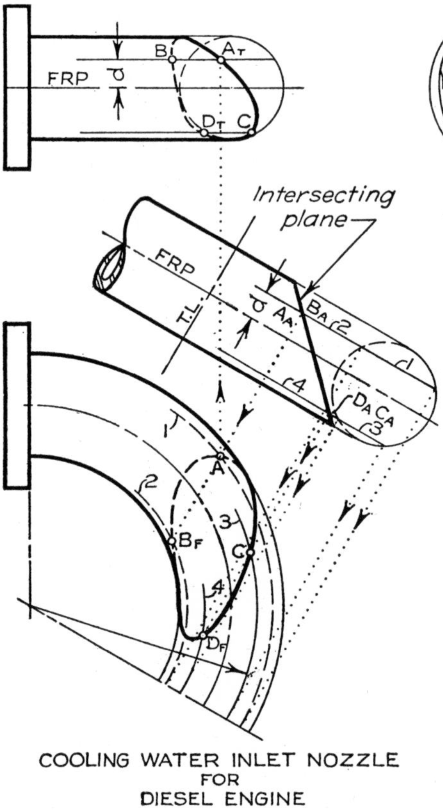

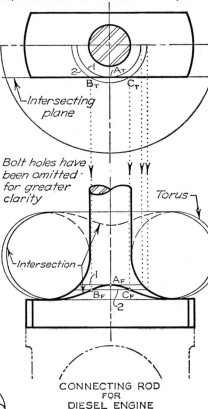

CONNECTING ROD
FOR
DIESEL ENGINE

Fig. 258. Application of a plane and torus intersection.

sion of the torus, which is necessary to determine the circular section of the torus in the auxiliary view. The axis of the torus *must* be true length in the *same* view that the plane appears in its edge view. Figure 110 illustrates how this may be obtained.

COOLING WATER INLET NOZZLE
FOR
DIESEL ENGINE

Fig. 259. Application of a plane and torus intersection.

Each cutting plane in the auxiliary view which appears in its edge view perpendicular to the true-length axis of the torus cuts two circles on the torus, one on the outside and the other on the inside of the torus.   The piercing points *A* and *B* of circles 1 and 2 with the edge view of the given plane are projected to the front view and onto the circular view of the circles.   A series of cutting planes is needed to find sufficient points on the curve of intersection.

191. PLANE AND SPHERE INTERSECTION

A plane intersecting a sphere always cuts a circle on the sphere *regardless* of the direction of the plane.

Two *HRP* planes intersecting the sphere of Fig. 260 intersect it in circles whose diameters are *AB* and *CE*.   The circles will, of course, appear true size in the top view.   An *FRP* intersects the sphere to create a circle of diameter *MN* which will be true size in the front view.

The circular intersection of a sphere with inclined or oblique planes will be true size in auxiliary views.

Figure 261 shows a rectangular slot cut through a partial sphere.   The radii of the arcs are as indicated.

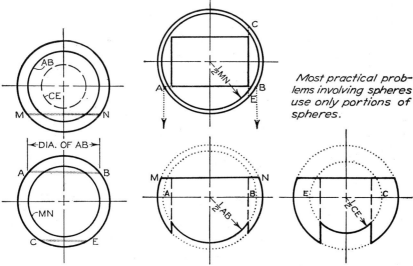

Most practical problems involving spheres use only portions of spheres.

The intersection of a plane with a sphere is ALWAYS a circle or arc.
Fig. 260. Plane and sphere intersection.

Practical problems involving intersections of planes and spheres are more readily solved if complete spheres and full circles for the intersections are drawn.
Fig. 261. Plane and sphere intersection.

192. THE GREAT CIRCLE

The **great circle** has the diameter of the globe and contains the center of the globe.

Figure 262 shows pictorially a great circle and a smaller diameter circle *M* on the globe through the two points *A* and *B*. The shortest distance on the globe from *A* to *B* is on the great circle and *not* on any smaller circle containing the two points. Figure 263 shows the smaller circle *M* revolved about a straight line through *AB* as an axis into the plane of the great circle. It is evident that the larger, and *not* the smaller, circle through *A* and *B* gives the shorter distance from *A* to *B*.

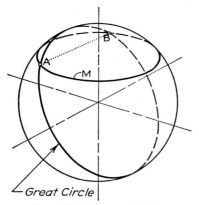

Fig. 262. The great circle.

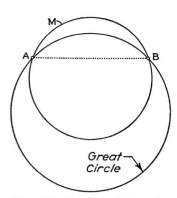

Fig. 263. Shortest distance between two points on the globe.

CHAPTER 15

DEVELOPMENTS, TRANSITIONS, AND THE HELIX

193. DEVELOPMENTS

The **development** of a surface is the unrolling of the surface onto a plane. The straight-line elements of the cylinder on the development will be parallel, while those of the cone will converge at a point. Developable surfaces are ruled, single-curved surfaces (see table in Fig. 225). Some *warped* surfaces may be *approximately* developed by a series of adjacent triangles representing the surfaces. Developments should have their *inside* face facing upward on the paper and so labeled. This is necessary because most sheet-metal rolling machines roll the ends upward; thus the top side becomes the inside. The elements should be indicated by fine lines in order definitely to establish the direction of roll.

Normally the shortest element is considered to be the best element to be used as the seam because it would require less welding, riveting, soldering, or brazing to seal the object. However, sometimes other considerations favor another element as the seam.

194. DEVELOPMENT OF A CYLINDER

In developing a cylinder two specific views are essential. They are the true-length view of the elements and their point view (point view of the center line or axis of the cylinder). Since the development is the true size of the surface, the true lengths of the elements are necessary. The distances between specified elements representing the surface are necessary. In Fig. 264 the center line (axis) of the cylinder is true length in the front view. In the auxiliary view the center line and the elements appear as points. The circular view of the cylinder is divided into twelve equal parts, and each number represents the end view of an element. Each numbered element should be represented in the true-length view of the elements in order that each length may be used in the development.

A section called a **right section** should be taken somewhere along the center line and *perpendicular* to the center line and elements in their *true-length* view. This right section in the development will stretch out as a straight line equal in length to the circumference of the end (point view of the center line) view of the cylinder. If the right section is a circle, its circumference is π times the diameter. If the right section is an ellipse, the approximate circumference of the ellipse is $\pi \sqrt{2(a^2 + b^2)}$, where a is one-half the minor axis and b is one-half the major axis.

Figure 264 explains the *accumulative error* if twelve or more chords are used to determine the stretch-out length of the right section instead of computing it.

When the development is placed in a semiauxiliary view position as shown, the elements are drawn perpendicular to the stretch-out line and their ends are determined by their projections from the front view. A *smooth* curve is then drawn through the ends of the elements.

If space does not permit the development to be put in a semiauxiliary view position, the stretch-out line can be drawn in *any convenient* place and the elements drawn perpendicular to it. The true lengths of the portions of the various elements on either side of the right section can be transferred by dividers instead of by projection.

See Fig. 283 for a development rolled into a cylinder. Note the element lines used to indicate the direction of roll.

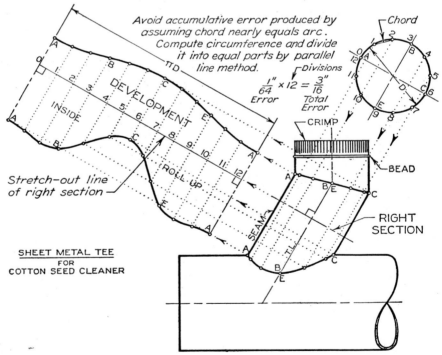

FIG. 264. Development of a cylinder.

195. TRUE LENGTH OF A DOUBLE-CURVED LINE (Development-of-a-cylinder Method)

The true length of *any double-curved* line may be determined and measured by assuming one view of the line to be the end view (point view of the elements) and right section of a right cylinder. In Fig. 265 the top view of the double-curved line is assumed to be the end view of a right cylinder; therefore all elements will be true length in the front view and each element will have one point of the curved line on it. For ease of solution make the bases of the cylinder perpendicular to the elements.

The stretch-out of the top view which is the right section of the cylinder is shown in the development of the cylinder to the right of the front view. The stretch-out line should be computed if possible. Each element that has been numbered is placed in the development. The point of the curve on element 1 in the front view is projected to the same element in the development. The point of the curve on element 8 is shown projected to the development. Intermediary elements such as *a*, *b*, and *c* may be chosen later if deemed necessary. A smooth curve is drawn through the points of the curve on the elements. The curve in the development is true length and may be measured with a map line-measuring device.

The development of a helix, which is a double-curved line, on a cylinder

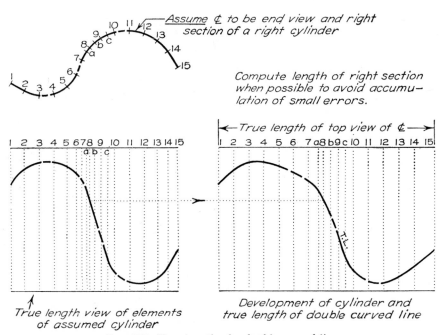

Fig. 265. True length of a double-curved line.

becomes a *straight* line upon the development of the cylinder. See Fig.
281 for further information.

196. DEVELOPMENT OF A RIGHT CIRCULAR CONE

The development of a right circular cone with all its elements of equal
length becomes a section of a circle as shown in Fig. 266*b*.   The radius
of the arc is the true length of the elements, and the angle is computed
using the formula in Fig. 266.   The computation of the angle α *eliminates
accumulation of error* inevitable when a series of chords is used.

Quadrant elements may be located on the development by dividing the
angle into halves and then dividing the halves.   Elements of an individual quadrant may be located by chords obtained from the circular view
of the cone and used in the development as shown with a minimum
accumulation of error.

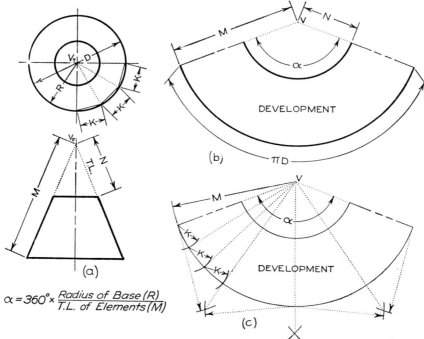

$$\alpha = 360° \times \frac{Radius\ of\ Base\ (R)}{T.L.\ of\ Elements\ (M)}$$

For greater accuracy in laying out the development, compute the angle α. Then divide the
development of the base πD into its quadrants
as shown in (c). The small error resulting from
using the chord "k" will be corrected at each
quadrant.

FIG. 266. Development of a right circular cone.

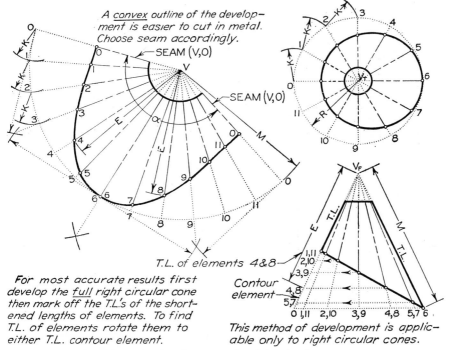

A *convex* outline of the development is easier to cut in metal.
Choose seam accordingly.

For most accurate results first
develop the *full* right circular cone
then mark off the T.L.'s of the shortened lengths of elements. To find
T.L. of elements rotate them to
either T.L. contour element.

This method of development is applicable only to right circular cones.

FIG. 267. Development of a right circular cone.

This method of making the development is applicable *only* to right circular cones.

Figure 267 shows a drawing of a right circular cone with the base cut off in an inclined position. The cone will be developed more accurately and quickly if it is developed on a right circular cone basis with all elements of length M and angle α computed. The cone is shown developed according to Fig. 266c. The circular view of the cone shows that twelve elements have been added. The lower ends of the elements, 0 to 11 inclusive, are then projected to the front view. The ends of the elements on the inclined base are located where the elements pierce the base. The true lengths of the elements may be considered to be revolved to the true-length contour elements simply by drawing the edge view of the circles of revolution parallel to the right circular base in the front view. Elements V_F4 and V_F8 are both E in length and may be measured accordingly along the corresponding elements of the development.

197. DEVELOPMENT OF AN OBLIQUE CONE

The development of an oblique circular cone is made by dividing the surface into a series of small triangles and then developing the triangles.

Each triangle uses two straight-line elements and a short chord subtending a small part of the base. One such triangle is shown in Fig. 268 as V-1-2, with V-1 and V-2 as the two straight-line elements and 1-2 as the small chord subtending arc 1-2. Each chord should be small enough so that for practical purposes it is equal to the arc it subtends. The chord is already true length in the top view.

The true lengths of the elements may be obtained by using the revolution method with V as the vertex of a series of cones of revolution and the bases in the same plane as the base of the oblique cone. The elements may be revolved so that they do *not* overlap the front view.

The series of true-length elements having one end in common, such as V_F, is called a **true-length diagram.**

The true-length diagram may also be created by constructing the right triangles shown in Fig. 102. V_F-A_F-4 is the right triangle for the true length of element V-4. The height of all elements is $V_F A_F$, one side of the right triangle. The other side is the measurement d_4, which is the length of element V-4 as it appears in the top view. The hypotenuse is the true length of element V-4.

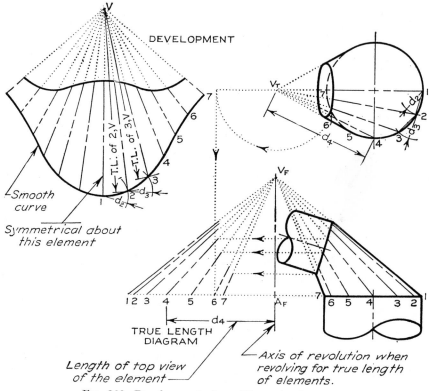

FIG. 268. Development of an oblique circular cone.

Since each element is shown true length in the true-length diagram, the upper end of each element may be projected to the true-length diagram.

The development is made by using the *full length* of each element and then locating points on the upper base by measuring the true lengths of the portions of the elements the problem requires. Triangles *V*-2-1 and *V*-3-2, etc., are developed as shown in the development. The elements should be shown on the development to indicate the direction of roll.

198. DEVELOPMENT OF A SPHERE

The only practical way to "develop" a sphere of any appreciable size is to divide the sphere into six equal segments and make one die to form the equal segments. It must be recognized that this is *not* a true development. The six equal segments face the six faces of an *inscribed* cube in the sphere. The corners of the cube locate the corners of the segments.

Draw two regular views of a cube as shown in Fig. 269 and an auxiliary view showing the *true length* of two of the diagonals of the cube. The diagonals of the cube will be the diameter of the sphere circumscribing the cube. The regular views of the cube locate the corners of the segments for that sphere.

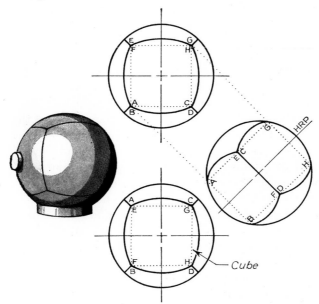

The surface of a sphere divided into equal segments (usually six) may have all of its segments formed by one die. An inscribed cube locates the four corners of each segment.

FIG. 269. Development of a sphere.

If a sphere of a different diameter is desired, extend the diagonals of the cube in the auxiliary view until they are equal in length to the diameter of the desired sphere. The cube may be enlarged to correspond to the new diagonals and the new diameter sphere and drawn in all views.

When it is inconvenient to make $\frac{1}{6}$ segment dies for larger spheres, each of the six equal segments may be subdivided into smaller patterns as shown in the photograph in Fig. 270. A and B are two corners of the six equal segments of Fig. 269. Note in Fig. 270 that each of the six segments have been subdivided into smaller pieces. There are several commonly used patterns of the subdivision.

FIG. 270. Pattern of development of a large sphere.

199. DEVELOPMENT OF A PRISM

A **prism** is basically a cylinder except that it has a limited number of edges (elements) and a finite distance between each whereas the cylinder has an infinite number of elements and the adjacent elements touch. The prism is also developed in much the same way that the cylinder is developed. The true length of the parallel edges (usually called **lateral edges**) must be determined, and the point view or end view of the parallel edges must be determined. A right-section stretch-out line is also used.

In Fig. 271 the lateral edges are true length in the auxiliary view projected off the front view. The point or end view of the lateral edges is in the secondary auxiliary view. The secondary auxiliary view gives the true size of the *right section* which is composed of the *perpendicular* distances between the parallel lateral edges. The right section appears in its edge view when the lateral edges are true length, is perpendicular to them, and may be represented *anywhere* along the lateral edges. Distance k indicates that the stretch-out line is composed of the sides of the right section of the secondary auxiliary view. The true lengths of the lateral edges relative to the right section are determined for the development by using measurements such as d and d_1, which were used to establish lateral edge $D4$. Corners such as C are located by measurements like k_1 and the perpendicular distance C_A is from the right section.

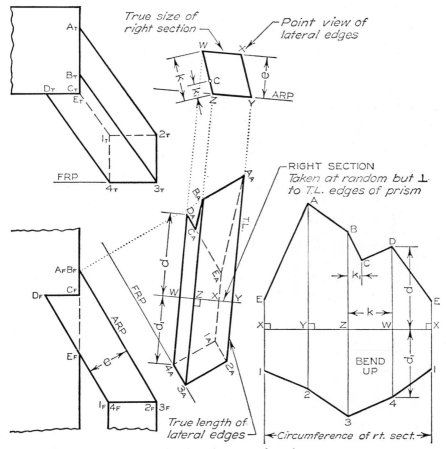

FIG. 271. Development of a prism.

200. DEVELOPMENT OF A PYRAMID

A pyramid is basically a cone except that it has a finite number of sides and edges (elements). The development of a pyramid is therefore similar to the development of a cone.

Figure 272 shows two methods of developing a pyramid. The drawing shows a truncated pyramid. One method uses the vertex of the pyramid, while the other does not.

The method using the vertex requires that the lateral edges be extended to the vertex V and that the true length of the lateral edges from the base of the pyramid to the vertex be determined by revolution or auxiliary view. Thus each face of the pyramid is a triangle which is composed of two lateral edges and one side of the base. The true lengths of VA, VB, and AB form one triangle.   The actual side of the object that is on this face may be determined by adding the true lengths of V-1 and V-2 to the two sides VA and VB of the triangle.   The remaining faces of the pyramid are similarly constructed.

The second method divides the four sides of each face of the truncated pyramid into two triangles by using either diagonal.   Face 3-4-C-D requires that the true length of the diagonal C-4 be determined in addition to the four sides bounding this face.   One triangle is constructed and then the next.   The inside of the development of the pyramid should face upward.

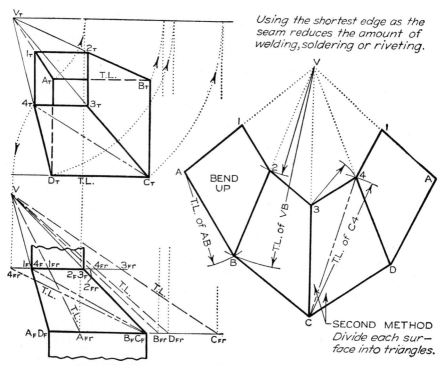

FIG. 272   Two methods of developing a pyramid.

201. APPROXIMATE DEVELOPMENT OF WARPED SURFACES

Warped surfaces may be approximated by dividing the surfaces into a series of triangles.   The surface will *not* be a smooth surface when constructed using this method.   It will actually be a series of small triangles bent along the adjoining sides of the triangles.   Examples of the approximate development of warped surfaces are explained in Arts. 204 and 205.

202. TRANSITIONS

A **transition** is a surface connecting two openings, such as pipes, of the same or different size and shape.   The transition may be a single surface or a combination of surfaces.

The truncated pyramid of Fig. 272 is a transition connecting two square pipes of different sizes.

Figures 302, 303, 305, and 306 show additional transitions.   They are applications of cone-shaped transitions.   In Fig. 305 the cone is tangent to the cylinder on both sides of the cylinder.

203. RECTANGLE-TO-CIRCLE TRANSITIONS

Figure 273 is a transition connecting a rectangular pipe with a circular pipe.   Although the transition could be constructed on the basis of a conoid, it is more practical to construct it with four triangular planes and four one-quadrant oblique circular cones.   For symmetry divide the circle into four quadrants and connect them to the corners of the rectangular pipe.

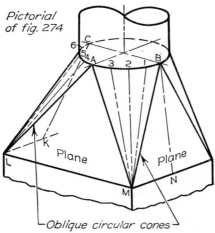

FIG. 273.   Rectangle-to-circle transition.

The orthographic views and development of Fig. 273 are shown in Fig. 274.   Since the transition is symmetrical about the horizontal center line of the top view, only one-half of the transition need be developed.   The triangle *BNM* will be a right triangle whose edges must be determined in their true lengths.

An oblique circular cone must be developed in the manner explained in Art. 197.   The oblique circular cone is developed by dividing the surface

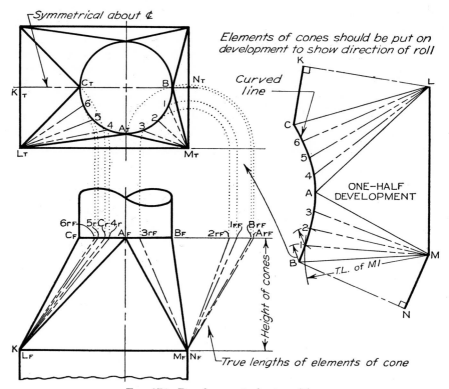

FIG. 274. Development of a transition.

into a series of small triangles. This is accomplished by dividing the base of the cone into several small parts as the oblique cone ABM of Fig. 274 shows. Each point chosen on the base of the cone is connected with the vertex to form sides of the series of triangles. Each element used as a side of the series of triangles must be determined in its true length by revolution.

After developing the triangular plane BNM, side BM is used as a side of a triangle representing one portion of the oblique cone. From M draw an arc of $M1$ radius, and from B draw an arc of $B1$ radius. Then develop the triangle $2M1$. Measurements B-1 and 1-2, etc., are already true length in the top view.

Figure 275 shows another rectangle-to-circle transition although the bases are not in parallel planes. The base of the cone is divided into quadrants as in Fig. 274, and the transition is likewise divided into triangular planes and one-quadrant oblique circular cones.

Two methods of revolving to find the true lengths of the elements of the cone are shown. In the case of the CML cone, each element is considered

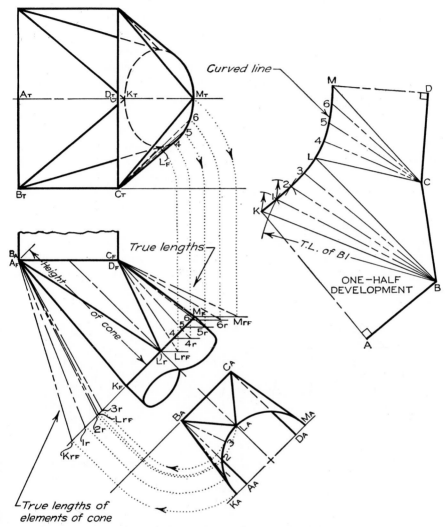

FIG. 275. Development of a transition.

in the revolution as a line *independent* of the surface of which it is a part. Each element of this cone is considered to be on a separate cone of revolution of its own vertical height in the front view.

The elements of cone *BKL* are considered to be on a series of cones of revolution with a common axis appearing as point B_A in the auxiliary view. The base plane of this series of cones of revolution is the plane of the circular base of the transition. The sides of the triangles on the base are true length in the auxiliary view. The development is then made as explained in Figs. 268 and 275.

204. WARPED-SURFACE TRANSITIONS

The approximate development of a warped-surface transition is made by dividing the surface into a series of small triangles as shown in Fig. 276. The series of points chosen on the larger base is connected by radial lines (compare with the warped cone and cow's horn in Figs. 248 and 249) to the point view of the axis. The circle is true size in the top view, while the other curve is foreshortened. Points chosen on the larger curve are *not* chosen on an equidistant basis in the top view. Some portions of the larger curve are foreshortened more than other portions. Note that C-6 is shorter than D-10 in the top view, yet they are approximately equispaced on the development which *is* the goal.

The radial lines divide the warped surface into a series of four-sided surfaces such as 1AC6. The four-sided surfaces are then divided into triangles by adding one diagonal. The diagonals are represented by different lines to make them easier to read. Since all points from A to B are at the same elevation, the upper ends of all elements may be placed together at R and to the right of the front view. The upper ends of the diagonals may be placed at another point such as S. The lower ends of

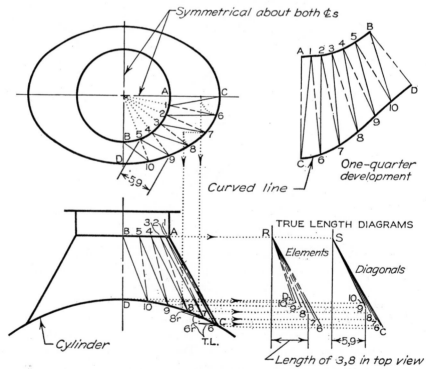

Fɪɢ. 276. Development of a warped-surface transition.

the elements and diagonals may be projected horizontally to the true-length diagrams. The vertical distances from R and S to the horizontal projections of the lower ends of the elements and diagonals give the heights of the right triangles for the true lengths of the lines as explained in Art. 77 and Fig. 102. The other side of each true-length right triangle is the length of each line as it appears in the *top* view. Note the measurement 5-9 in the top view and its use in the diagonal diagram. The hypotenuse S-9 is the true length of the line. The sheet metal will be bent along the elements and the diagonals, and for that reason the surface will *not* be smooth. The elements and the diagonals will need to be represented on the development.

205. REVERSE-DIRECTION ELBOW

The inside and outside of the elbow (or transition) of Fig. 277 are cylindrical surfaces. The outline of these two surfaces is based on the helix which, when developed, becomes a straight line as explained in Art. 209. The one-half lead from A to G and the circumference of the one-half cylinder, which is $\pi \times$ radius N, determine the helix angle.

The surfaces between the semicircles are *right helicoids*, which are

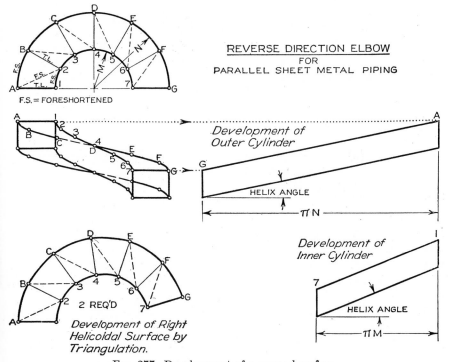

FIG. 277. Development of a warped surface.

warped surfaces. The radial elements are represented by solid lines, and the diagonals by dashed lines. Because *none* of the sides of the triangles are true length in either view, each one must be revolved for its true length.

206. CYLINDRICAL-PIPE ELBOW

A cylindrical-pipe elbow is a multiple-cylinder transition. If the center lines of the several cylinders are tangent to the circular center line of the elbow, the cylinders will be *right* circular cylinders as shown in Fig. 278*b*. If the center lines of the cylinders are used as chords of the circular center line, the cylinders will be *oblique* circular cylinders. Compare the two drawings, and note where the connecting cylinders end and their shapes.

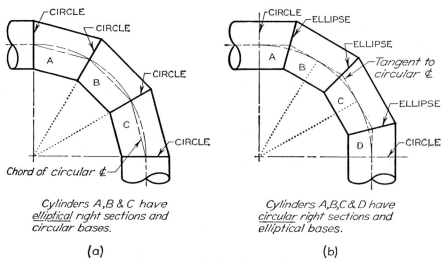

Cylinders A, B & C have *elliptical* right sections and circular bases.

Cylinders A, B, C & D have *circular* right sections and elliptical bases.

(a)   (b)

Fɪɢ. 278. Cylindrical-pipe elbows.

207. CONICAL TRANSITIONS

A conical transition is a developable surface and therefore can be rolled in the factory. It produces better results than the triangulation of warped surfaces and, since it can be rolled, costs less to manufacture. A right circular cone is preferred to an oblique circular cone.

Right circular cone transitions are shown in Figs. 302; 303; 305*b*, *c*, *d*, and *e*; and 306*a* and *b*. They are developed as explained in Art. 196.

An *oblique circular* cone can be used to greater advantage in a circle-to-circle transition where the circles are in *nonparallel* planes than a warped-surface transition. This is possible because circles may appear in two directions on an oblique circular cone. They are shown in Fig. 279. The drawing shows how the second direction is obtained.

Regardless of the angular relation of the two cylinders or their relative diameters, if their center lines intersect, an oblique circular cone transition may be used.

It is necessary to establish the circles on their respective center lines through the use of a sphere with its center at E, the intersection of the center lines. The size of the sphere determines how far the circles must be from point E. This is based on the fact that any two circles, regardless of their diameters on the surface of a sphere, form an oblique or a right circular cone when connected.

In Fig. 280 a sphere of *convenient* size is drawn with its center at E. It intersects both of the given right circular cylinders in two circles AB and RS. Extend RA and SB to locate the vertex of the oblique circular cone. This cone may be developed as explained in Art. 197.

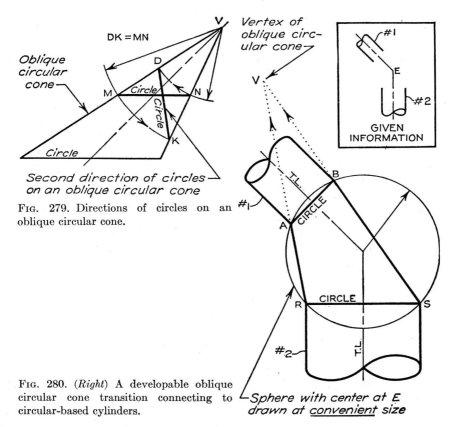

FIG. 279. Directions of circles on an oblique circular cone.

FIG. 280. (*Right*) A developable oblique circular cone transition connecting to circular-based cylinders.

208. HELIX

A *helix* is a *double-curved* line (it does not lie in a plane) appearing on a surface of revolution in such a manner that it travels around its axis of revolution at a uniform angular rate and along the axis (or surface) at a uniform linear rate.

The *lead* of a helix is the advancement measured *along* the axis of the surface of revolution for 360° of travel around the axis.

209. HELIX ON A CYLINDER

In Fig. 281 the amount of the lead is indicated. The lead is divided into the *same* number of equal spaces that the circular view is divided into angular spaces. The number of spaces depends upon the size of the surface of revolution. The starting point is 0. In traveling from 0 to 1, which is 30° about the axis, the point travels from 0 to 1 along the axis or $\frac{1}{12}$ of the lead. The circular view of point 1 is projected to the front view, then point 2 is projected, and so on.

The development of the cylinder shows the helix to be a *straight* line at a *constant* angle to the base of the cylinder. This angle is called the **helix angle.** It is a very important angle in accurate thread and gear work

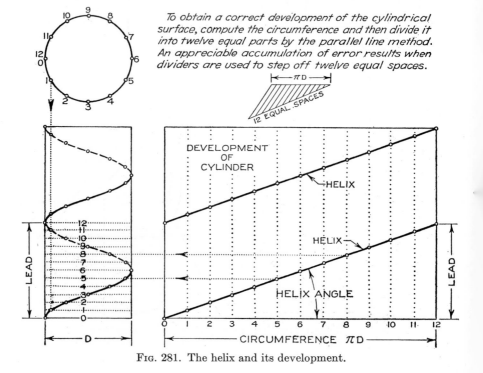

FIG. 281. The helix and its development.

and is computed to seconds of a degree. The points of the front view could have been determined by projecting the intersection points of the numbered elements of the developed cylinder with the helix line from the development to the front view. The helix can be determined by a right triangle created by the circumference of the circle, πD, and the lead.

Figure 282 shows pictorially the lead and development of one turn of a helix.

Figure 283 shows a cylinder being rolled. Before it was rolled, the plate stock was a parallelogram. The edge BD of

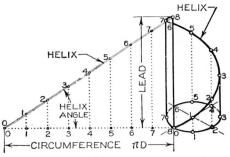

FIG. 282. Development of a helix.

the parallelogram becomes a helix after the plate stock is rolled. The straight line AC upon being rolled will match with BD. The helix angle for this helix is BAC.

The path that A would traverse from its present position if it could be

FIG. 283. A helix and its development.

rolled around by hand to B would be an involute curve. The straight line AC would generate a convolute surface as explained in Art. 170.

210. RIGHT-HAND AND LEFT-HAND HELICES

The helices of Figs. 281 and 282 are right hand. A *right-hand* helix advances away from the end of the helix in a *clockwise* direction. A *left-hand* helix advances away from the end of the helix in a *counterclockwise* direction. See Fig. 284 for a pictorial view of both helices.

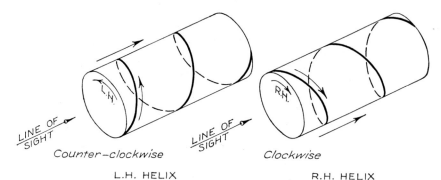

Counter–clockwise   Clockwise

L.H. HELIX   R.H. HELIX

FIG. 284. R. H. and L. H. helices.

211. HELIX ON A CONE

A helix on a cone traverses around the cone at a uniform angular rate and along the axis at a uniform linear rate. The circular view of the cone in Fig. 285 is divided into twelve equal divisions, and the lead along the axis is likewise divided into twelve equal divisions. The top view points of the helix are determined first and then projected to the front view. At position 7 along the axis the point of the helix is on a circle of the cone of the indicated diameter. Point 7 on the helix in the top view is at the intersection of the No. 7 circle and the No. 7 straight-line element. This point is then projected to the front view of the circle at No. 7 position along the axis.

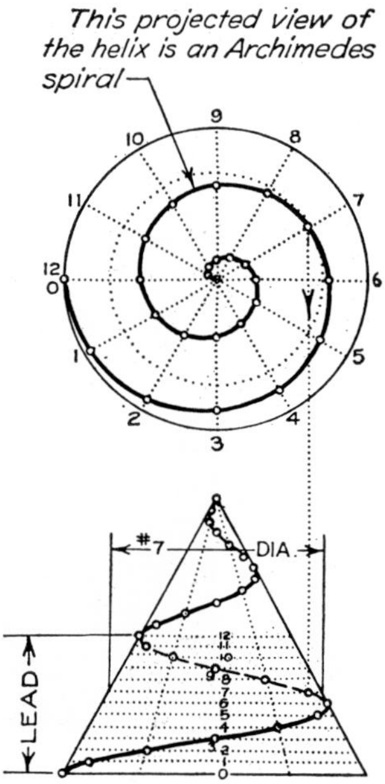

This projected view of the helix is an Archimedes spiral

212. HELIX ON A SURFACE OF REVOLUTION

The end or circular view of the double-curved surface of revolution in Fig. 286 is divided in the same way that the cone and cylinder are divided. The lead may be

FIG. 285. The helix on a cone.

measured either along the
curved outline of the front
view or along the axis as
the problem dictates.   The
diameters of the circles for
the various positions from 0
to 12 in the front view are
determined from that view
and drawn as circles in the
top view.   Where each circle intersects its radial line
of the top view is that
view's position of the point
on the helix.   Each point
is then projected to its own
edge view of the circle in
the front view.   The edges
of the worm gear teeth are
helices.

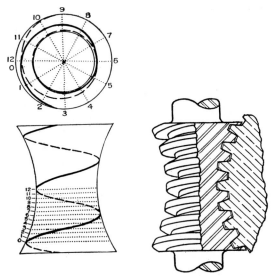

FIG. 286. The helix on a warped surface of
revolution.

213. DEVELOPMENT OF A CYLINDER USING THE HELIX ANGLE

A helical-wound cylinder, as shown in Fig. 287, is a structurally stronger
cylinder but not so economical to manufacture as the cylinder developed
in Fig. 281.

The width of the standard rectangular plate stock and the number of
pieces which are to form the width of the development determine the
helix angle.

The helix angle for this development is determined by laying off the
stretch-out of the circumference of the right section of the cylinder which
is πD.   Then divide this stretch-out circumference line into the *same*
number of equal parts that the width of the development is to be divided

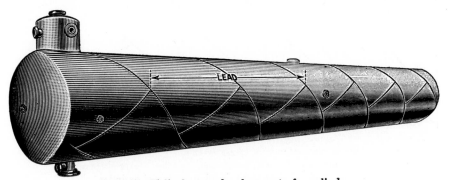

FIG. 287. Helical seam development of a cylinder.

into rectangular pieces. The width of the development of Fig. 288 is composed of two A-width pieces; therefore the stretch-out circumference line is likewise divided into two equal parts.

Strike off two arcs of A and $2A$ radii from one end of the stretch-out line as shown. From the other end of the stretch-out line draw a line tangent to the arc of $2A$ radius and another line from the equal part division mark on the stretch-out line tangent to the arc of A radius. The lines tangent to arcs of A and $2A$ radii are parallel and form sides of the rectangular strips; the angle they make with the stretch-out line is the *helix angle*. The helix angle may also be computed.

If the development were to have three A-width pieces to create its width, the stretch-out circumference line would have to be divided into three equal parts and a third arc drawn of $3A$ radius.

The elements need to be drawn on the development to indicate the direction of roll. The stripes on a barber pole may be laid out and painted on its development in a similar manner.

Figure 283 shows another method of shaping the development of a cylinder. The size of the parallelogram will be the circumference of the cylinder by the length of the cylinder and by the desired helix angle BAC. Some long cylinders are constructed by using several of these cylinders welded end to end.

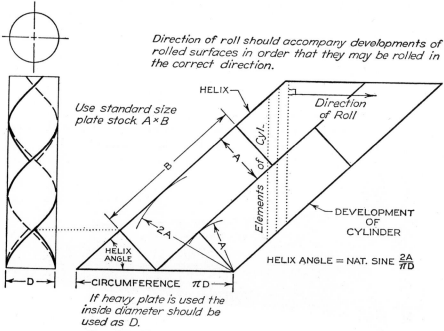

Direction of roll should accompany developments of rolled surfaces in order that they may be rolled in the correct direction.

Use standard size plate stock $A \times B$

HELIX

Direction of Roll

DEVELOPMENT OF CYLINDER

HELIX ANGLE = NAT. SINE $\dfrac{2A}{\pi D}$

HELIX ANGLE

Elements of Cyl.

CIRCUMFERENCE πD

If heavy plate is used the inside diameter should be used as D.

FIG. 288. Helical seam development of a cylinder.

CHAPTER 16

INTERSECTION OF SURFACES

214. BASIC METHODS

The line of intersection of two surfaces is similar to that of two planes. Lines of each plane pierce the other plane along the line of intersection. Straight- and curved-line elements on each curved surface also intersect the other curved surface along the line of intersection.

The methods used in solving for the line of intersection of two curved surfaces vary in their application depending upon whether the problem is theoretical or practical.

A series of cutting planes is used in solving most intersection of surfaces problems and cuts either straight-line or circular elements on the surfaces. A cutting plane may cut straight-line elements on one surface and *either* straight-line or circular elements on the other surface. In any case, the elements, whether they are straight lines or circles, lie on the same cutting plane as well as on their respective surfaces and intersect to create points on the curve of intersection of the two surfaces. A series of cutting planes properly spaced will supply a sufficient number of points through which the line of intersection may be drawn.

Practical applications of intersections of surfaces frequently do *not* use all of each theoretical intersection. This may be observed in the several applications in this chapter and pictorially in Fig. 289, where cylinder A, if it were in a theoretical problem, would pass all the way through the vertical cylindrical tank and the spherical cap of the other tank.

FIG. 289. The difference between theoretical and practical intersection problems.

215. DETERMINING WHERE A CURVE OF INTERSECTION CHANGES VISIBILITY

The following items are applicable to all intersections of surfaces:

1. A curve of intersection changes visibility *only* at its point of tangency with a contour element. Examples: any of the intersection illustrations.

2. Opposite ends of the visible portion of a curve need *not* be on contour elements of the same object. Example: D of Fig. 290 is on a contour element of the cylinder, while C is on a contour element of the cone, and B and A are on the same contour element.

3. To find the points of tangency of the curve with the contour elements, take cutting planes that will contain the contour elements.

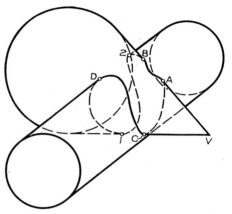

Fig. 290. Determining where a line of intersection changes visibility.

216. CHOICE OF CUTTING PLANES

If the cutting planes of Fig. 291 were all taken equispaced, the points on the line of intersection would have been quite erratic in their locations. The straight-line elements of a cylinder and a cone cut by a specific cutting plane are determined by their ends on the base of the cylinder and cone.

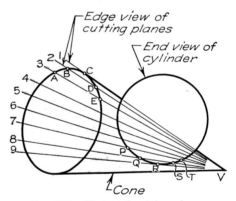

Fig. 291. Choice of cutting planes.

The edge view of plane 1 of Fig. 291 is tangent to the cone; thus it establishes only one element on the cone and two on the cylinder. Assume that cutting plane 2 was omitted. Although planes 1 and 3 are not far apart, nevertheless the elements through points A and E are a considerable distance from element C. Thus from A to E there is only one element. Cutting plane 2 corrects this discrepancy.

Cutting plane 9 is tangent to the cylinder and thus produces only the one element R. This would be the only element from P to T if cutting plane 8 were omitted.

217. DETERMINING THE VISIBILITY OF POINTS ON THE LINE OF INTERSECTION

A point to be visible on the line of intersection in a given orthographic view or on a pictorial *must* be on two visible elements with one element on one object and the other element on the other object. The visibility of the elements on either object should be considered *independently* of the other object, that is, as if the other object did not exist. Referring to Fig. 292 the visibility of the four points *A*, *B*, *C*, and *D* is determined as follows:

A is visible because it is on two visible elements.

B is invisible because it is on one invisible element.

C is invisible because it is on two invisible elements.

D is invisible because it is on one invisible element.

If a point is on an invisible element, it is invisible in that view although it is on a visible element of another object.

The cutting plane of Fig. 292 shows that the elements cut by this plane are determined by the intersection of the cutting plane with each base plane. As the series of cutting planes approaches a plane tangent to either object, the cutting planes should be closer together.

218. INTERSECTION OF TWO CYLINDERS
(Cutting-plane Method)

A cutting plane parallel to the axis of a cylinder will cut along two straight-line elements. The cutting plane in Fig. 293 is parallel to the axes of two cylinders and cuts

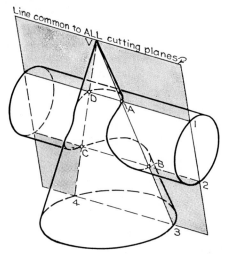

FIG. 292. Determining the visibility of points on the line of intersection.

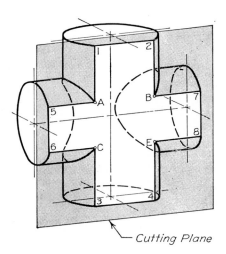

A cutting plane parallel to the center-lines of both cylinders cuts straight line elements on both. The intersection of the cutting plane with the bases locates the ends of the elements. Points A,B,C and E are points on the curve of intersection of the two cylinders.

FIG. 293. Intersection of two cylinders.

along two straight-line elements on each cylinder. The two elements 1-3 and 2-4 of one cylinder intersect the two elements 5-7 and 6-8 of the other cylinder to create the four points A, B, C, and E on the line of intersection. A series of parallel planes is needed to establish a sufficient number of points on the line of intersection.

Figure 294 is an application of a two-cylinder intersection. The

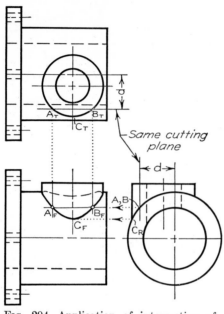

cutting plane represented is parallel to both axes. The cutting plane intersects the base of one cylinder in the top view. This intersection locates one end of each of the two elements of the cylinder which lie on the cutting plane. This same cutting plane intersects the base of the other cylinder in the side view. These elements are then drawn in the front view where they intersect at points A and B, two points on the line of intersection.

The limiting cutting plane which is tangent to the front of the vertical cylinder will locate the lowest point on the curve in the front view.

In Fig. 294 each axis appears in its point view in either the top or the side views. In Fig. 295

Fig. 294. Application of intersection of two cylinders.

neither axis appears in its point view in either the top or front view. The axis (£) of cylinder 1 appears in its point view in the auxiliary view. All cutting planes parallel to this axis will appear in their edge views in this view. When the edge views of this series of cutting planes are taken parallel to the axis of cylinder 2, each cutting plane will cut straight-line elements on both cylinders.

The cutting plane represented in the auxiliary view by a fine solid line intersects one base of cylinder 2 at points 1 and 2 and cylinder 1 at points 3 and 4. These points are projected to the top view, and the elements through them are drawn parallel to their respective axes. They intersect to create four points P, Q, R, and S on the line of intersection.

Element 2 will be more accurately located (see Fig. 334) in the top view by first locating 2 in the front view on the base of cylinder 2 using the dimension d.

The points of intersection P, Q, R, and S in the front view, when located by the intersection of the front view of the elements, should, of course, be directly below the top view of the same points.   If they are not, there is either inaccuracy or error in the solving of the problem.   This check should *always* be made.

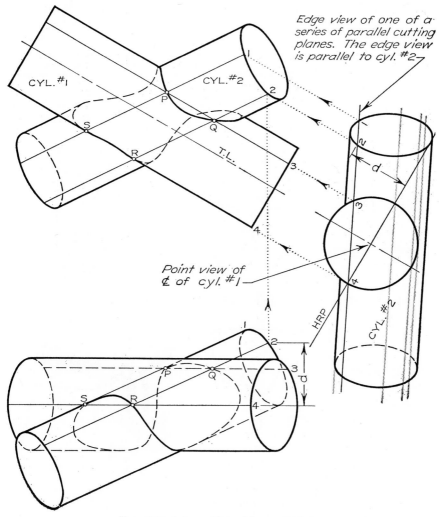

FIG. 295.   Intersection of two cylinders.

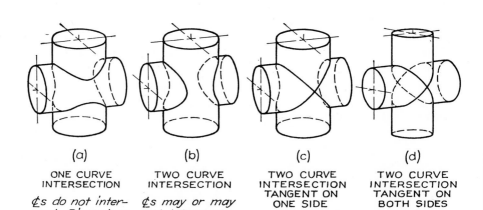

(a)	(b)	(c)	(d)
ONE CURVE INTERSECTION	TWO CURVE INTERSECTION	TWO CURVE INTERSECTION TANGENT ON ONE SIDE	TWO CURVE INTERSECTION TANGENT ON BOTH SIDES
₵s do not intersect. Diameters may or may not be equal.	*₵s may or may not intersect. Different size diameters.*	*₵s do not intersect. Different size diameters.*	*₵s intersect. Same size diameters.*

FIG. 296. Types of intersections of two cylinders.

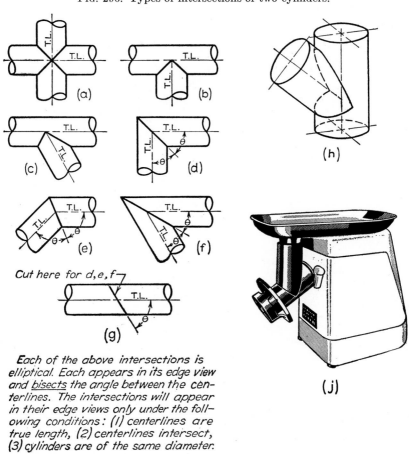

Each of the above intersections is elliptical. Each appears in its edge view and <u>bisects</u> the angle between the centerlines. The intersections will appear in their edge views only under the following conditions: (1) centerlines are true length, (2) centerlines intersect, (3) cylinders are of the same diameter.

FIG. 297. Applications of intersections of two cylinders of the same diameter.

219. TYPES OF INTERSECTIONS OF TWO CYLINDERS

Figure 296 shows the several intersections created by two intersecting cylinders.   Cylinders intersecting at acute angles create similar results.

Figure 297 shows several practical applications of Fig. 296d.

Several practical applications of two-cylinder intersections are shown in Fig. 298.   In Fig. 298b the smaller cylinder is tangent on one side to the larger cylinder.   The intersection will be pointed at the tangency point.   Compare it with Fig. 296c.   The intersections, as they appear in the top view of Fig. 298c, are hyperbolas, but spatially they are double-curved lines, that is, lines which do not lie in a plane.

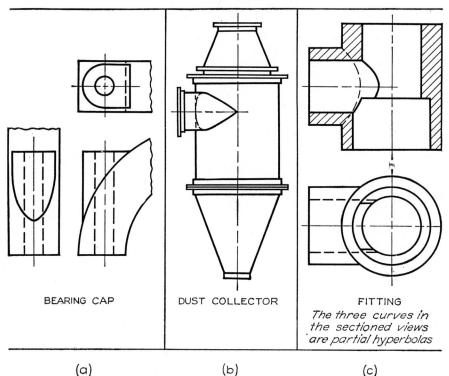

BEARING CAP   DUST COLLECTOR   FITTING
The three curves in the sectioned views are partial hyperbolas

(a)   (b)   (c)

FIG. 298. Applications of two-cylinder intersections.

220. APPLICATION OF A TWO-CYLINDER INTERSECTION

Figure 299 is an application of two intersecting cylinders. There are portions of the application that do not influence the intersection. They should be *omitted* from the steps in obtaining the solution.

Figure 300 shows and explains the steps used to solve the problem of Fig. 299. Note that several portions of Fig. 299 were omitted for clarity purposes.

Cylinder *CE* appears in its circular view in the auxiliary view. The cutting planes appear in their edge view in this view and are parallel to the axis of the *AB* cylinder. These two cylinders are tangent to each other on opposite sides as shown in Fig. 296*d* and parts *h* and *j* of Fig. 297.

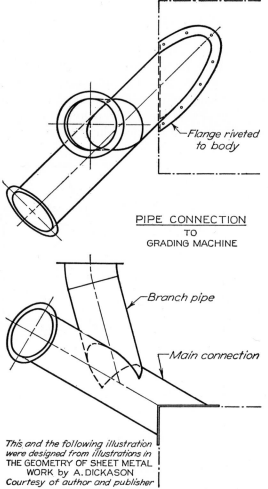

Flange riveted to body

PIPE CONNECTION
TO
GRADING MACHINE

Branch pipe

Main connection

This and the following illustration were designed from illustrations in THE GEOMETRY OF SHEET METAL WORK by A. DICKASON
Courtesy of author and publisher

It is most common to find in practical problems that only a portion of the theoretical intersection is used. In the above intersection one-half of the theoretical intersection is used. See the following illustration for the method of finding the intersection.

FIG. 299. Application of two-cylinder intersection.

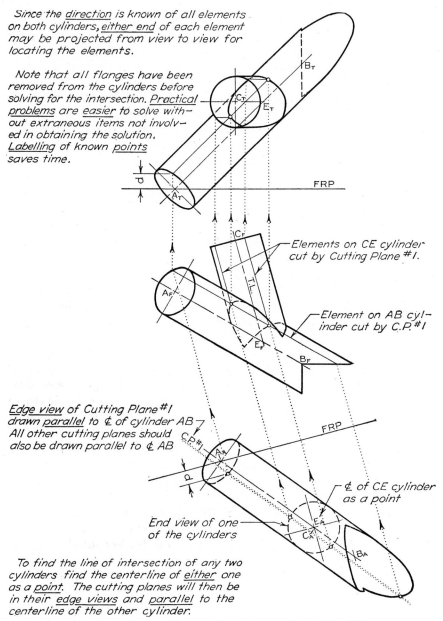

Since the *direction* is known of all elements
on both cylinders, *either end* of each element
may be projected from view to view for
locating the elements.

Note that all flanges have been
removed from the cylinders before
solving for the intersection. *Practical
problems* are *easier* to solve with—
out extraneous items not involv—
ed in obtaining the solution.
Labelling of known *points*
saves time.

Elements on CE cylinder
cut by Cutting Plane #1.

Element on AB cyl—
inder cut by C.P. #1

Edge view of Cutting Plane #1
drawn *parallel* to ₵ of cylinder AB
All other cutting planes should
also be drawn parallel to ₵ AB

₵ of CE cylinder
as a point

End view of one
of the cylinders

To find the line of intersection of any two
cylinders find the centerline of *either* one
as a *point*. The cutting planes will then be
in their *edge views* and *parallel* to the
centerline of the other cylinder.

FIG. 300. Solution of two-cylinder intersection of Fig. 299.

221. INTERSECTION OF TWO OBLIQUE CYLINDERS WITH A COMMON BASE PLANE

As previously explained, in order to cut straight-line elements on two cylinders by a cutting plane, the cutting plane must be parallel to both cylinders. In Fig. 301 a *trial* cutting plane is drawn through a conveniently chosen point A and is parallel to both cylinders. All cutting planes will be parallel to the trial cutting plane. The trial cutting plane intersects a plane parallel to the base plane containing one base of each cylinder along line BC. A series of parallel planes intersecting a single plane will intersect it in parallel lines. Thus all cutting planes will intersect the base plane in lines parallel to $B_T C_T$.

A line which is parallel to $B_T C_T$ and intersects the two bases lying in the *same* plane locates one end of each of the four elements cut by one cutting plane. Thus points 1, 2, 3, and 4 of the top view are the lower ends of four elements. The line parallel to $B_T C_T$ that located these four points and the elements through them create one cutting plane. These four elements, since they lie in one plane, intersect to create the four points P, Q, R, and S on the line of intersection. The front view of the same four elements through the front view of points 1, 2, 3, and 4 locates the front view of the four points P, Q, R, and S. If the front view of each of these four points does not line up vertically with their corresponding top views, an inaccuracy or error exists.

A line which is parallel to $B_T C_T$ and crosses the two visible ends of the cylinders in the top view would *not* produce elements lying in one plane. The two visible circles are not in the same plane, but the lower bases of the two cylinders do lie in the same plane. In order to use the visible circles, one cylinder would have to be shortened or the other lengthened until the new base lies in the same base plane as that of the other cylinder.

This problem could have been solved by a series of cutting planes parallel to the plane of the bases which would have cut circles on each cylinder. Points on the line of intersection would be located where the two circles on a cutting plane intersect.

In Fig. 309 two lines converge at PP. If PP is ignored and the two lines assumed to be parallel, it is apparent that this illustration equally well applies to two-cylinder intersections. For further information see Art. 228.

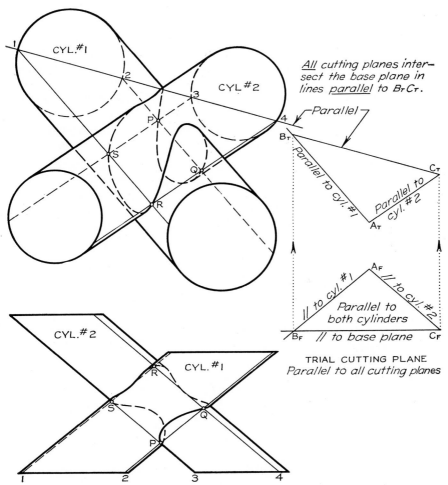

FIG. 301. Intersection of two oblique cylinders with a common base plane.

222. INTERSECTION OF A CYLINDER WITH A CONE (Cutting-plane Method)

In order that a cutting plane may cut straight-line elements on a cone, the plane must pass through the vertex of the cone; thus the vertex of the cone will be on all cutting planes. The series of cutting planes must be parallel to the cylinder in order to cut straight-line elements on the cylinder.

In the auxiliary view of Fig. 302 the cylinder appears in its circular view and the axis ($\mathbf{t}$) in its point view. All cutting planes cutting straight-line elements on a cylinder and a cone appear in their edge views in this view with the edge view radiating from V_A.

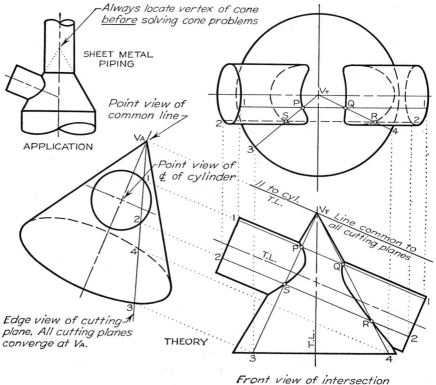

FIG. 302. Intersection of a cylinder with a cone and application.

The cutting plane shown in its edge view in the auxiliary view intersects the bases of both objects at points 1, 2, 3, and 4. These four points on their respective objects locate the four elements lying on this cutting plane. They intersect at points P, Q, R, and S as four points on the curve of intersection.

The series of cutting planes has one line in common. It is a line which is parallel to the cylinder and passes through the vertex of the cone. This line is shown pictorially in Fig. 292.

223. INTERSECTION OF CYLINDER AND CONE WITH PARALLEL AXES

In Fig. 303 the cutting planes will appear in their edge views through V_T, since both axes appear in their point views in the top view. One such cutting plane is represented in the top view. Points 1 and 2 locate the lower ends of the elements cut on the cone, while P and Q locate the elements of the cylinder. The intersection of these four elements gives the two points P and Q on the curve of intersection. The front view of this intersection is a parabola, while the top view is a circle. Spatially, the curve is a double-curved line. Note the completion of the cones in the application. This is necessary in order to solve the problem. Vertices of cones seldom appear on practical applications.

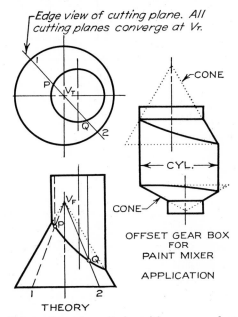

FIG. 303. Intersection of a cylinder with a cone and application.

224. TANGENT CYLINDER AND CONE INTERSECTIONS

A cone tangent to the opposite sides of a cylinder *always* has two ellipses as the line of intersection as shown in the pictorial of Fig. 304.   When *both* axes appear true length in the same view, the two ellipses will appear in their edge views and cross at the tangency points.   The cutting planes will appear in their edge views through V_T in the top view.

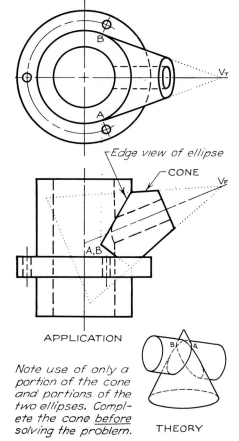

225. SPHERE METHOD OF ESTABLISHING A CONE TANGENT TO A CYLINDER

The cone tangent to a cylinder makes an excellent transition from one cylinder to another.   Its size may be determined by a sphere or spheres tangent to the cylinder or cylinders and the cone.

Figure 305a shows a tangent cone and cylinder.   Assuming the size of the cylinder to be given, the cone is drawn tangent to the cylinder in the *circular* view of the cylinder.   A sphere of the diameter of the cylinder with its center at the intersection of the axes would be tangent to both objects as shown in Fig. 305b.

In Fig. 305b the tangent cone

Note use of only a portion of the cone and portions of the two ellipses. Complete the cone before solving the problem.

Fig. 304. Application of cylinder and cone intersection.

is used as a transition between two cylinders.   A sphere with its center at the intersection of the axes and tangent to the cylinder establishes the size of the cone with the base of the cone given as shown.   This application uses a portion of each of the two ellipses of the line of intersection.

Figure 305c is another application of Figs. 305a and b but uses one full ellipse and none of the other.

Figure 305d eliminates the perpendicular axes of the cone and the

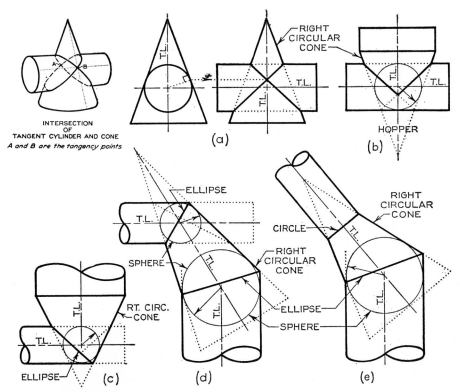

The intersections shown in the pictorial are ellipses. Practical applications invariably require the use of only one ellipse or a portion of both ellipses. When right circular cones are to be used, their size may be determined by the spheres which can be inscribed in both objects. The ellipse intersection occurs when the centerlines intersect and the cylinder and cone are tangent on opposite sides. The edge views of the ellipses appear when both centerlines are true length.

FIG. 305. Applications of tangent cylinder and cone intersections.

cylinder of the above illustrations. This permits easier flow through the junction. The included axis of the cone *must intersect* the axes of both cylinders. Two spheres with their centers as shown are necessary to establish the size of this right circular cone.

Figure 305e requires only one tangent sphere to establish the size of the cone.

These cones should be developed according to Figs. 266 and 267.

The tangent sphere method is applicable *only* to *right circular* cones and cylinders.

226. CYLINDER AND CONE INTERSECTIONS

In Fig. 306*a* when the vertex of the cone is inside the cylinder, the intersection is *not* an ellipse.   But when one element of the cylinder *coincides* with an element of the cone, the intersection *is* an ellipse as shown in Fig. 306*b*.

Figure 306*c* shows a cone with its base given on the large cylinder while the cone is tangent to the small cylinder.   The size of the cone is determined first in the *circular* view of the cylinder.   The cone is an *oblique circular* cone, since the axis is at an acute angle to the base.   The intersection with the smaller cylinder is an ellipse.   The sphere method of establishing the cone does *not* apply.   Note the difference between the shape of this cone and those of Figs. 305*d* and *e*. Fig. 307 is an application of Fig. 306*c*.

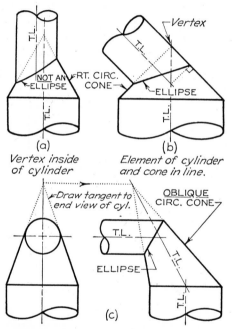

(a)
Vertex inside of cylinder

(b)
Element of cylinder and cone in line.

(c)

Locate vertex of oblique circular cone by drawing contour elements tangent to end view of cylinder. Inscribed sphere does not apply.

Fɪɢ. 306. Applications of tangent cylinder and cone intersections.

Fɪɢ. 307. Application of a tangent cylinder and oblique cone intersection.

227. INTERSECTION OF AN OBLIQUE CYLINDER AND OBLIQUE CONE WITH A COMMON BASE PLANE

In Fig. 308 a base of the cylinder is in the same plane as the base of the cone.   The line common to all cutting planes cutting straight-line elements on both objects passes through the vertex of the cone and is parallel

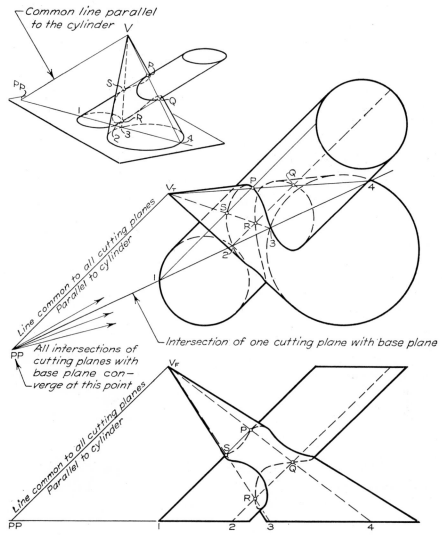

FIG. 308. Intersection of a cylinder and cone with a common base plane.

to the cylinder. This common line pierces the base plane at *PP*. The series of cutting planes will cut the base plane in straight lines which converge at the piercing point *PP*.

A line which is drawn through the top view of *PP* intersects both bases lying in the common base plane and will locate one end of each of four elements. Such a line is shown in Fig. 308, and it locates points 1 and 2 on the cylinder and 3 and 4 on the cone. Elements through these points will lie in one cutting plane created by the common line and the line through *PP* which located the points 1, 2, 3, and 4.

Points 1 and 2 are on one of the two lines establishing the cutting plane, and the elements through them are parallel to the common line; therefore they are on the same plane.   Points 3 and 4 are on the same line as points 1 and 2, and the elements through them end at *V* on the common line. These four lines intersect at *P*, *Q*, *R*, and *S*, which are four points on the line of intersection. A series of these planes properly spaced will give sufficient points through which to draw the line of intersection.

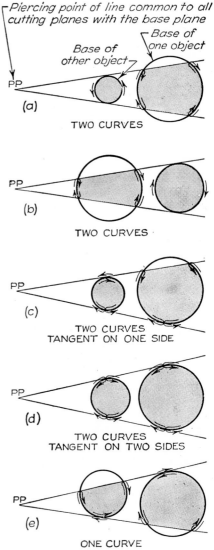

(a)

TWO CURVES

(b)

TWO CURVES

(c)

TWO CURVES
TANGENT ON ONE SIDE

(d)

TWO CURVES
TANGENT ON TWO SIDES

(e)

ONE CURVE

FIG. 309. Determining in advance the type of intersection.

228. DETERMINING THE TYPE OF INTERSECTION BEFORE SOLVING THE PROBLEM

Whether the line of intersection is a continuous curve (one curve), two separate curves, two curves tangent on one side, or two curves tangent on both sides depends on the tangent cutting planes.

Since one end of each element cut by a cutting plane is located by the straight line of intersection of that cutting plane with the base plane, these lines of intersection which are tangent to the bases can determine the nature of the line of intersection of the two objects.

The several parts of Fig. 309 are applicable to cylinder with cone and cone with cone intersections. The circles represent bases of cones or cylinders of the above intersections. *PP* is the piercing point of the common line of all cutting planes with the *single* base plane.

In Fig. 309*a* the two cutting plane intersections through *PP* with the base plane are tangent to the same object, and both cutting planes intersect the other object. The elements ending on the larger based object outside either tangent plane do not pierce the other object. Every element of the smaller based object pierces the larger object, but there are elements on opposite sides of the larger based object which separate the entrance from the exit points as the elements go through the larger object. Figure 310 shows a two-curve intersection where every element of the cone pierces the cylinder. There are elements ending on opposite sides of the base of the cylinder which are outside either plane tangent to the cone.

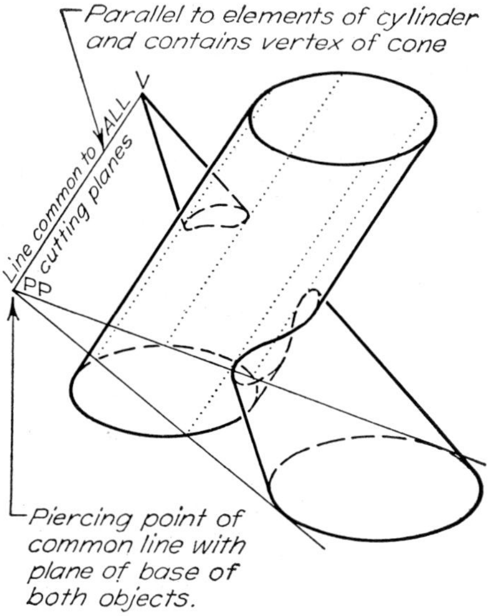

Figure 309*b* is similar to Fig. 309*a* and produces similar results.

Figure 309*c* shows one cutting plane tangent to both objects while the other tangent plane is tangent to one object but intersects the other. All elements of the smaller based object pierce the larger based object. All elements except those which end outside the one tangent cutting plane pierce the smaller based object. Figure 311 shows two tangent cutting planes similar to those of Fig. 309*c*. The two curves touch at the indicated point of tangency. The lines of intersection at this point *always* form an X and are *not* two rounded curves touching each other.

Parallel to elements of cylinder and contains vertex of cone

Line common to ALL cutting planes

Piercing point of common line with plane of base of both objects.

FIG. 310. A two-curve intersection.

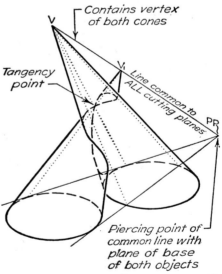

Contains vertex of both cones

Tangency point

Line common to ALL cutting planes

Piercing point of common line with plane of base of both objects

FIG. 311. Two curves tangent on one side intersection.

Figure 309*d* creates two objects tangent to each other on opposite sides as shown in Figs. 304 and 305 and makes the transitions of these two figures practical to use.

Figure 309*e* determines a continuous-curve intersection (one curve). Figures 292 and 308 show one-curve intersections.

229. INTERSECTION OF A CYLINDER WITH A CONE WITH THE BASES IN SEPARATE PLANES

When the base of the cone does not lie in the plane of either base of the cylinder, the piercing points are located where the common line (through the vertex and parallel to the cylinder) pierces *both* base planes. This is shown in Fig. 312, where PP_1 is the piercing point of the common line with one base plane of the cylinder and PP_2 is the piercing point of the common line with the base plane of the cone.

The line of intersection of the two base planes must be found. A series of points such as A *must* be chosen *along the line of intersection of the two base planes*. A-PP_1-PP_2 represents one cutting plane. A-PP_1 lies in the plane of the base of the cylinder and intersects its base at points 1 and 2 which are ends of the two elements of the cylinder cut by this cutting plane. They are on this cutting plane, because points 1 and 2 are on a line of the plane, and the two elements are parallel to the common line of the plane. A-PP_2 lies in the plane of the cone's base and intersects its base at points 3 and 4 which, when connected with V, are the two elements on the cone cut by this cutting plane. The elements through points 1, 2, 3, and 4 intersect at points P, Q, R, and S on the line of intersection.

Other cutting planes are established by taking a series of points on the line of intersection of the two base planes and connecting them with the piercing points PP_1 and PP_2.

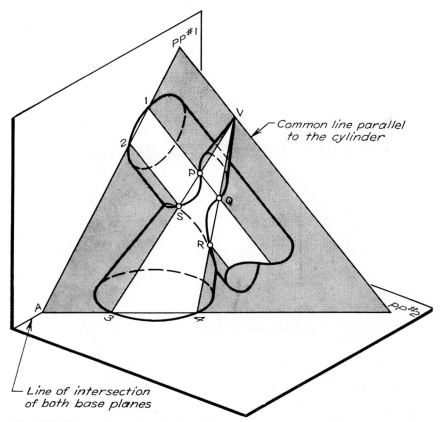

FIG. 312. Intersection of a cylinder with a cone having perpendicular base planes.

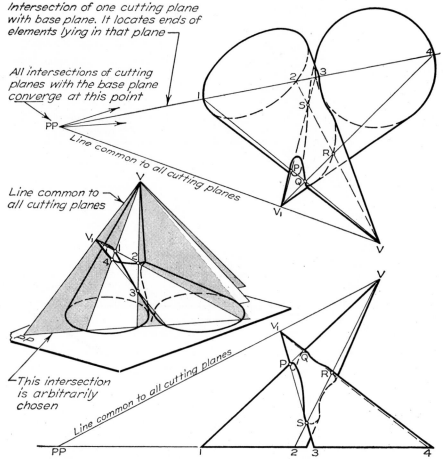

Intersection of one cutting plane with base plane. It locates ends of elements lying in that plane

All intersections of cutting planes with the base plane converge at this point

Line common to all cutting planes

Line common to all cutting planes

This intersection is arbitrarily chosen

Line common to all cutting planes

FIG. 313. Intersection of two cones having a common base plane.

230. INTERSECTION OF TWO CONES (Cutting-plane Method)

There is a line common to all cutting planes cutting straight-line elements on two intersecting cones. The common line passes through both vertices. In Fig. 313 the bases of both cones have a common base plane. The series of cutting planes intersect the base plane in lines which converge at the piercing point PP where the common line pierces the base plane.

The elements cut on the two cones by each cutting plane are located by drawing a line through PP that intersects both bases. One such line locates points 1, 2, 3, and 4 in the top view. The elements through these points intersect at points P, Q, R, and S.

231. INTERSECTION OF TWO CONES WITH BASES IN SEPARATE PLANES

The piercing points of the common line passing through both vertices pierce the two base planes of Fig. 314 at PP_1 and PP_2. The line of intersection of the two base planes is needed. A series of points K along the line of intersection of both base planes as shown in the pictorial establishes each cutting plane. In order that K-PP_1 and K-PP_2 lie in the base planes and intersect with the bases, point K *must* be taken on the line of intersection of the two base planes. The cutting plane K-PP_1-PP_2 intersects the base of one cone at points 1 and 2 and the base of the other cone at points 3 and 4. The elements through these four points are

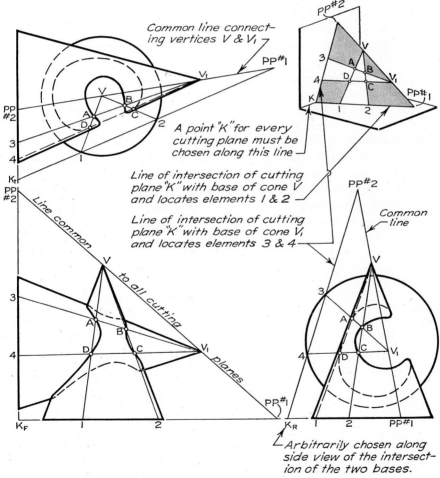

FIG. 314. Intersection of two cones having perpendicular base planes.

shown pictorially, and they intersect to create four points A, B, C, and D on the line of intersection of the two cones.

Every point of the cutting plane in the pictorial is located in the three orthographic views. Point K may be arbitrarily chosen in either the top or side view. If K_R is arbitrarily chosen along the line of intersection of the two base planes, K_T must be located in the top view by the distance K_R is from an FRP. The front view of K_R-PP_2 shows that it lies in the base plane of one of the two cones. The front view also shows that K_T-PP_1 lies in the base plane of the other cone.

232. INTERSECTION OF A CYLINDER WITH A TORUS

When the axes of a cylinder and a torus are parallel or perpendicular, the points on the line of intersection are readily obtained by a series of cutting planes perpendicular to the axis of the torus. The cutting planes in this position will cut circles on the torus and either circles or straight lines on the cylinders.

The cutting plane represented in Fig. 315a cuts two circles on the torus, one circle on one cylinder, and two straight lines on the other cylinder.

A, B, C, and E are four points on the line of intersection and are on the edge view of the cutting plane in the front view. All circles on the left cylinder coincide in the top view. The two straight-line elements of the cylinder to the right intersect only the larger circle of the cutting plane at points R and S and create two points on the line of intersection. Note that the intersection of the cylinder to the right comes to a point which is the point of tangency of the cylinder with the torus. See Fig. 316 for two examples of this point of tangency.

Figure 315b shows three applications of the intersection of a cylinder with a torus. For the intersection of a cylinder with its axis skewed to the axis of the torus see Art. 235 (also see Fig. 323b).

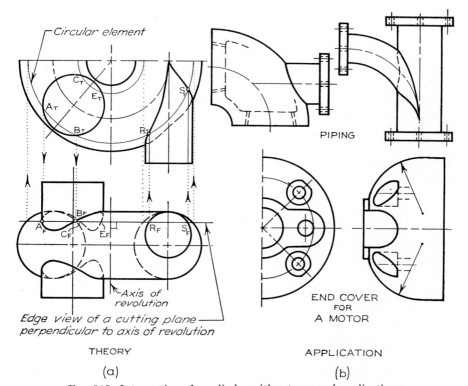

THEORY

(a)

APPLICATION

(b)

FIG. 315. Intersection of a cylinder with a torus and applications.

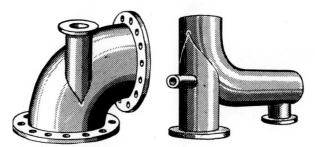

FIG. 316. Applications of cylinder and torus intersection.

233. INTERSECTION OF A CYLINDER WITH A SPHERE

The cutting planes used in obtaining the intersection of a cylinder with a sphere should be so taken that they will cut either circles or straight lines on the cylinder and be true size in one of the views. If the planes are taken parallel to the cylinder and parallel to the plane of one of the views (the view may be an auxiliary view), the circles cut by the cutting planes on the sphere will be true size. Otherwise ellipses will need to be drawn.

In Fig. 317 a series of frontal planes will cut straight lines on the cylinders and circles on the spheres which may be drawn as circles in the front view. In Fig. 317c the circle intersects only one of the two elements on the cylinder cut by the cutting plane. As shown in Fig. 317a the line of intersection of a cylinder with a sphere having its center on the axis of the cylinder is two circles perpendicular to the axis. This is the basis of the sphere method explained in Art. 235. In the view where the plane of the center of the sphere and the axis of the cylinder is true size, the view of the line of intersection will appear as a parabola as in Figs. 317b, c, and d.

In Fig. 318 the circular view of the cylinder appears in the auxiliary view. A series of cutting planes parallel to HRP will cut the sphere in circles which will appear as circles in the top view. When a cutting

This illustration courtesy of Prof. Angel Taibo, Buenos Aires, Argentina

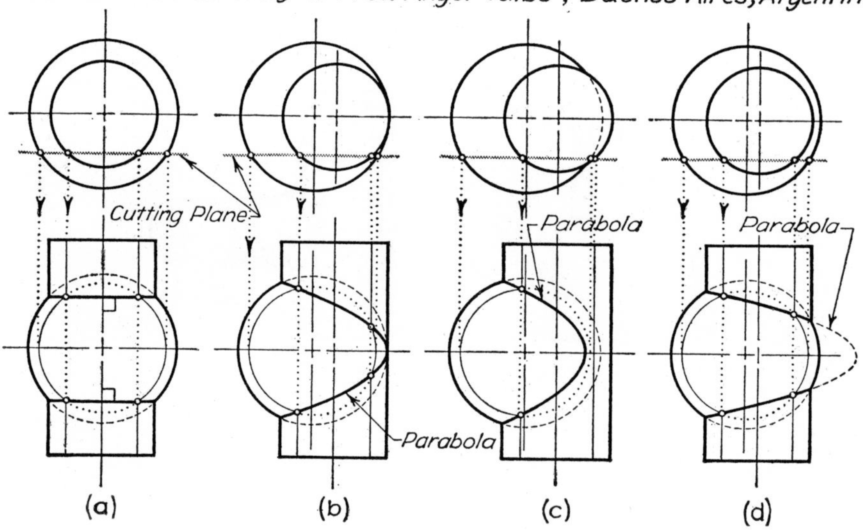

(a) (b) (c) (d)

FIG. 317. Intersection of a cylinder with a sphere.

plane is taken through C_A, which is the intersection of the cylinder with the outline of the sphere, an inflection point is obtained. Note its position in the top and front views. The curve reverses its direction at C.

Figure 319a is an application of the intersection of a cylinder with a sphere. The indicated cutting plane is taken parallel to the axis of the cylinder and in a frontal plane position. In order to establish the radius of the circle cut on the sphere, the *great circle* of the sphere *must* appear in the view where the edge view of the cutting plane appears. For all practical purposes this is true in the top view

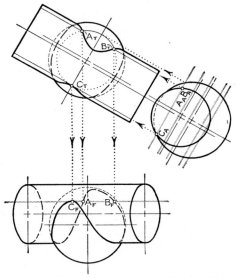

FIG. 318. Intersection of a cylinder with a sphere.

of this practical problem. Another application is shown in Fig. 319b.

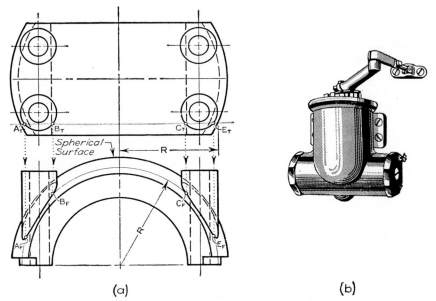

(a) (b)

FIG. 319. Application of a cylinder and sphere intersection.

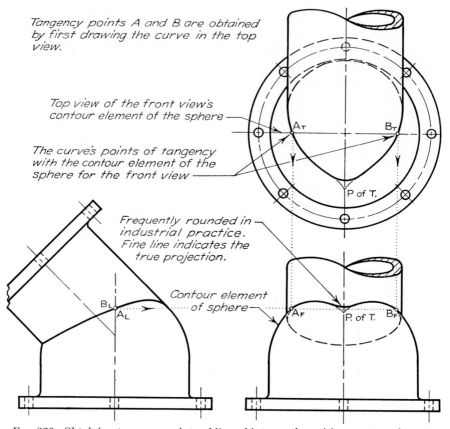

Tangency points A and B are obtained by first drawing the curve in the top view.

Top view of the front view's contour element of the sphere

The curve's points of tangency with the contour element of the sphere for the front view

Frequently rounded in industrial practice. Fine line indicates the true projection.

Contour element of sphere

FIG. 320. Obtaining tangency points of line of intersection with a contour element.

234. LOCATING TANGENCY POINTS OF THE LINE OF INTERSECTION WITH CONTOUR ELEMENTS

To locate the tangency points of the line of intersection with contour elements of two ruled surfaces, take cutting planes through the ends of these elements. In some cases involving double-curved surfaces this is not easily done.

In Fig. 320 a circular view of the cylinder was used to obtain points on the line of intersection. The line of intersection is tangent at points A and B to the contour element of the sphere in the front view. It is difficult to establish in the auxiliary view the correct cutting plane or planes which will locate A and B.

The contour element of the front view of the sphere appears in its edge view in the top view and coincides with the horizontal center line through the center of the sphere. Points A_T and B_T are at the intersection of the top view of this contour element with the top view of the line of intersection. These two points, when projected to the front view of the contour element, are the points of tangency of the line of intersection with the contour element of the sphere. This same contour element appears in the side view along the vertical center line of the sphere. Points A_L and B_L coincide at the intersection of the side view of this contour element with the line of intersection.

The side view of the line of intersection of the cylinder with the sphere appears as a parabola. Turn the book until the axis of the cylinder appears vertical, and then compare the line of intersection with the upper half of Fig. 317b.

235. CUTTING-SPHERE METHOD TO OBTAIN LINES OF INTERSECTION

A series of concentric cutting spheres (in contrast to cutting planes) may be used to find the line of intersection of *intersecting surfaces of revolution* provided the axes of revolution intersect and are *both* true length in the same view. The point of intersection of the two axes is used as the center of the series of cutting spheres. Each cutting sphere cuts circles on both intersecting surfaces of revolution. Points on the line of intersection are at the intersection points of one circle with another circle. When both axes appear true length in the same view, the circles on the cutting spheres will appear in their edge views. The points on the line of intersection are where the edge views of the circles intersect.

Figure 321 shows the intersection of a sphere having its center on the axis of revolution of each of three surfaces of revolution. When the axis of revolution is true length, the intersection of the sphere with each surface of revolution is two circles AB and MN appearing in their edge views and perpendicular to the axis of revolution.

Figure 322 is a combination of Figs. 321a and c. In order that the series of cutting spheres cut circles on both objects, the centers of the spheres must be at the intersection of the axes (℄). The largest sphere intersects the cylinder to create the edge view of the circle C. The same sphere intersects the double-curved surface of revolution in the two circles A and B, which also appear in their edge views. The edge view of circle C intersects the edge views of circles A and B for points on the line of intersection.

The inflection point of the line of intersection is obtained by a cutting sphere *tangent* to the double-curved surface of revolution. The edge view of circle 2 is the line of tangency. This same cutting sphere intersects the cylinder at circle 1. The point of inflection is where the edge views of circles 1 and 2 intersect.

In Fig. 323a cutting sphere I cuts circles A and B on the double-curved

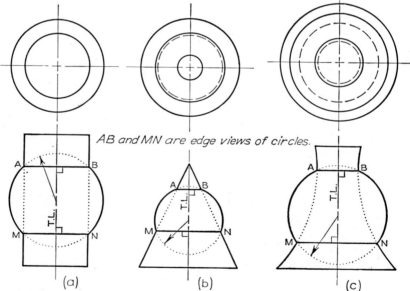

AB and MN are edge views of circles.

(a)   (b)   (c)

A sphere intersecting a cylinder, cone or double curved surface of revolution which has its center on the centerline of the other object intersects it in two circles which will appear as straight lines when the centerline is true length.

Fig. 321. Cutting-sphere intersections.

surface of revolution. It also cuts circle G on the cone and circle C on the cylinder. Circle A intersects circle C to create point 1 on the line of intersection as shown. Circle A intersects circle G to create point 4 on another line of intersection as shown. Neither circle C nor G intersects circle B. In other words, circle B does not pierce the cone or the cylinder. Cutting sphere II cuts similar circles, all appearing in their edge views as did cutting sphere I.

Figure 323b shows that the cutting-sphere method applies to certain cylinder and torus intersections. The cutting sphere cuts circles A and B on the torus and circle C on the cylinder. Circle C intersects circle A at point 1 but does not intersect circle B.

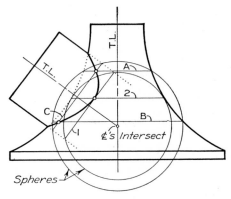

Circles A and B are on the surface of revolution and on the larger sphere. Circle C is on the cylinder and on the same sphere. The three circles A,B & C lying on the larger sphere intersect to give points on the curve of intersection of the cylinder with the surface of revolution. The centerlines must intersect and should appear true length or the circles will appear as ellipses.

FIG. 322. Cylinder and double-curved surface of revolution intersection: cutting-sphere method.

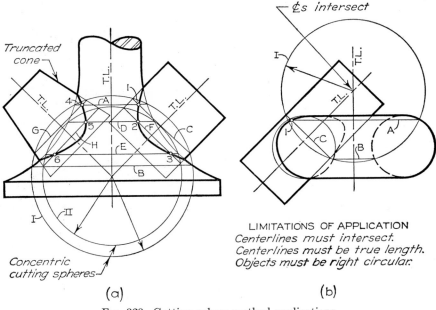

(a)   (b)

FIG. 323. Cutting-sphere method applications.

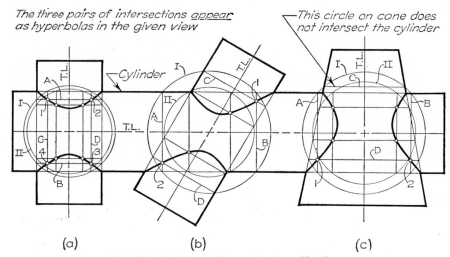

FIG. 324. Cutting-sphere method applications.

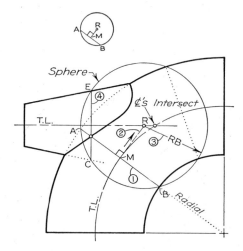

A sphere intersecting a torus will have a circle as the curve of intersection *only* when the center of the sphere is on a line *tangent* to the centerline of the torus. The sequence of steps in establishing points on the curve of intersection of the cone and torus are numbered. A separate "R" must be located for each sphere.

FIG. 325. Cone and torus intersection: cutting-sphere method.

Figure 324 shows three intersections obtained by the cutting-sphere method.

Figure 325 shows the cutting-sphere method applied to cone and torus intersection. A cutting sphere with its center on a *circular* center line (contrast this to the axis of revolution of Fig. 323*b*) of a torus will *not* intersect the torus in a circle.   Instead, the center of the sphere must be on a line tangent to the circular center line of the torus.

The *position* of the circle on the torus and the axis of the cone determine the location and size of the cutting sphere; thus, the cutting sphere is *not* drawn first.   First, draw the edge view of circle AB *radially* as shown. Through its center M draw a line tangent to the circular center line of the torus and extend the tangent line until it intersects the axis of the cone at point R.   Point R is the center of the cutting sphere which will cut the circle AB on the torus and also cut circle CE on the cone.   Circles CE and AB intersect to create a point on the line of intersection.

236. PARALLEL-CYLINDER METHOD TO OBTAIN INTERSECTIONS OF CYLINDERS WITH SURFACES OF REVOLUTION

The parallel-cylinder method to obtain the line of intersection of a cylinder with a cone, torus, sphere, or other surfaces of revolution employs the two straight lines of intersection of two parallel cylinders. A cylinder is constructed using as its base a *circular element* on the surface of revolution and is drawn *parallel* to the given cylinder.

Let circular element RS of the torus of Fig. 326 be one base of an oblique circular cylinder to be constructed *parallel* to the given cylinder. The other base of this newly constructed cylinder is drawn at a convenient elevation but *parallel* to the base circle RS.   The given cylinder MK is extended to the same plane that contains the upper base of the newly constructed cylinder.   The new base of the extended cylinder MK is an ellipse.   See Fig. 328, which shows how to cut off a cylinder, extended or shortened.

The elliptical base of the extended given cylinder has its center at N. The upper circular base of the constructed cylinder whose lower base is circle RS has its center at E.   Note that the axis CE of the newly constructed cylinder is *parallel* to axis MKN in *all* views.   The elliptical base with its center at N and the circular base with its center at E intersect at points 1 and 2.   The two parallel cylinders intersect along two straight-line elements through points 1 and 2 parallel to the axes of the cylinders.   The two straight-line elements through points 1 and 2 end on the circle RS at points A and B.

Points *A* and *B*, since they are on the circle *RS*, are on the surface of the torus.   Points *A* and *B*, since they are on two straight-line elements of the given cylinder, are on the surface of that cylinder.   Thus these two points, since they are on the given cylinder and the torus, are on the line of intersection of the two objects.

A series of circles on the torus similar to *RS* and taken on the inside as well as the outside of the torus may be used as bases of a series of *parallel* cylinders all *parallel* to the given cylinder.   The upper bases of these oblique circular cylinders, as they intersect the elliptical base of the extended given cylinder at points similar to 1 and 2, locate the upper ends of elements similar to elements 1-*A* and 2-*B*.   The lower ends of the elements, as they end on their respective circles on the torus, furnish additional points on the line of intersection.

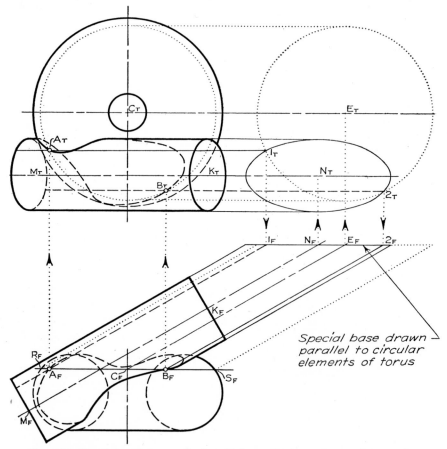

FIG. 326. Parallel-cylinder method applied to cylinder and torus intersection.

The top view of the points such as A and B are projected from the front view either onto the straight-line elements through 1 and 2 or onto the top view of circle RS.

Both points A and B are on the upper half of the torus, and A is on the upper half of the cylinder. Thus A is visible in the top view, but B is invisible because it is on the lower half of the cylinder.

Figure 327 shows pictorially a cylinder similar to the given cylinder of Fig. 326. The upper end of this cylinder has been extended to a horizontal plane which is parallel to the circular elements of another object, one of which is represented by circle RS.

An oblique circular cylinder with circle RS as its lower base is constructed parallel to the given cylinder. The upper base, which also is a circle, is in the *same* plane as the base of the extended given cylinder. These two bases intersect at points 1 and 2. The elements are 1-A and 2-B. A and B are on the given cylinder and on the circle RS, which is an element of either a cone, torus, sphere, or other surface of revolution. Thus A and B are two points on the line of intersection of the given cylinder with any surface of revolution of which circle RS is a part.

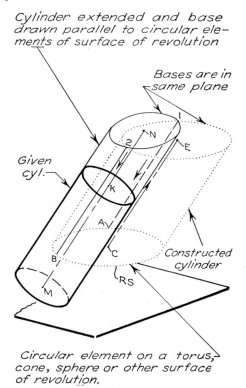

Cylinder extended and base drawn parallel to circular elements of surface of revolution

Bases are in same plane

Given cyl.

Constructed cylinder

Circular element on a torus, cone, sphere or other surface of revolution.

FIG. 327. Parallel-cylinder method.

237. EXTENDING OR CUTTING OFF A CYLINDER TO OBTAIN A PREFERRED BASE

Frequently either base of a given cylinder is *not* convenient to use. Another base may be substituted by either extending or cutting off the given cylinder.

Assume that in Fig. 328 a horizontal base is desired at the indicated elevation. The major and minor axes of the elliptical base may be readily obtained if the *true length* of the cylinder is obtained. AB of the auxiliary view and the diameter of the cylinder establish the minor axis, while CD establishes the major axis. The ellipse may now be drawn by the concentric-circle or trammel method shown in Fig. 186.

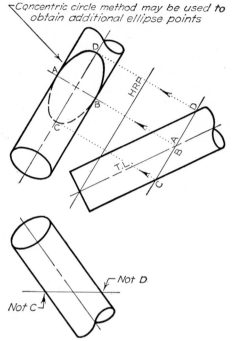

FIG. 328. Establishing a useful base on a cylinder.

238. PRACTICAL APPLICATION OF PARALLEL-CYLINDER METHOD

The only feasible method to solve for the intersection of the cylinder with the torus of Fig. 329 is the parallel-cylinder method. Two of a series of parallel cylinders with each having as one of its bases a circular element of the torus and each cylinder to be constructed parallel to the given cylinder are to be explained. The auxiliary view is taken to show the true-size *circular* view of the circular elements of the torus. The special base for the given cylinder is *parallel* to the *circular* elements of the torus and is also true size in the auxiliary view.

Since only part of the torus is given, only the radii of the circular elements are used. $C_T E_T$ is a circular element on the torus, and its center is at C_T. $C_T E_T K_T R_T$ represents one view of an oblique circular cylinder with one base as $C_T E_T$ on the torus and the other base $R_T K_T$ in the same plane as the special base of the cylinder. Radius N is the radius of the circle at position $C_T E_T$ on the torus. The arc of radius N with R_A as the center is the circular view of the other base of the constructed parallel cylinder. This arc, since it is in the *same* plane as the elliptical base of the cylinder, intersects the ellipse base of the given cylinder at point 1. Point 1 projected to the top view is one end of the straight-line element of intersection of the parallel cylinders. An element through point 1 parallel to the given cylinder ends on the edge view of the circle of the torus at A_T, which is one point on the line of intersection.

The circle on the inside of the torus is of $C_T F_T$ radius and otherwise indicated as radius M. $C_T F_T G_T R_T$, a constructed cylinder with one of its bases on the torus at $C_T F_T$, is parallel to the given cylinder, and its other base $R_T G_T$ is in the plane of the *special base* of the given cylinder. An arc of radius M with its center at R_A in the auxiliary view represents the base of the constructed cylinder that is in the plane of the ellipse. This

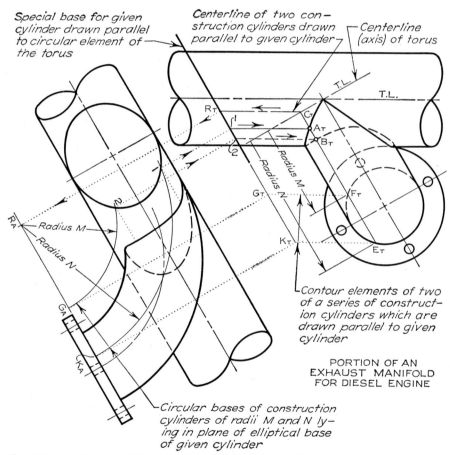

Special base for given cylinder drawn parallel to circular element of the torus

Centerline of two construction cylinders drawn parallel to given cylinder

Centerline (axis) of torus

Contour elements of two of a series of construction cylinders which are drawn parallel to given cylinder

PORTION OF AN EXHAUST MANIFOLD FOR DIESEL ENGINE

Circular bases of construction cylinders of radii M and N lying in plane of elliptical base of given cylinder

FIG. 329. Application of the intersection of a cylinder with a torus: parallel-cylinder method.

circular base intersects the ellipse base at point 2. Point 2 projected to the top view is one end of the line of intersection of the two parallel cylinders. The other end of the element through point 2 is point B_T. Point B_T is another point on the line of intersection.

If the line of intersection is required in the auxiliary view, points A_A and B_A are on the two straight-line elements of the given cylinder through points 1 and 2. Carefully compare this solution with Figs. 326 and 327, for they apply directly to Fig. 329.

CHAPTER 17

GRAPHICAL ACCURACY

239. GRAPHICAL ACCURACY

There are limitations as to how accurate a drawing may be made. Seemingly minute errors in the equipment, width of the pencil lines, minute errors in measurements, etc., produce errors which on occasion become magnified and may produce results *far* from correct.

In most drafting work if a line or a point is located within $\frac{1}{64}$ in. of the correct position of the line or point, the line or point is considered accurately located. Accuracy of draftsmanship consistently held to $\frac{1}{100}$ in. is very high-quality work.

240. EQUIPMENT ERRORS

An error of 1° in an angle of a triangle will produce, as shown in Fig. 330, an *unseen* error of nearly $\frac{3}{16}$ in. in a 10-in. projection line. Such an error is difficult to locate unless one questions the accuracy of his equipment. A small damaged corner of a triangle, as shown in Fig. 331b, if not corrected will produce a similar error.

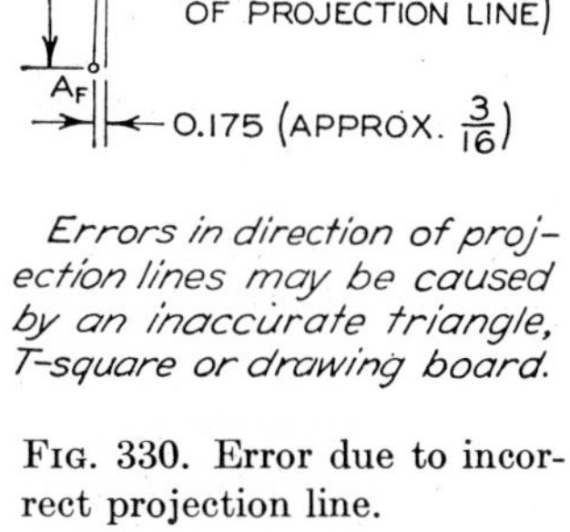

Figure 331a points out that the pencil point should be kept in the "corner" of the triangle as shown. Plastic triangles and T squares should be checked for their accuracy *every few months*. They may be corrected by rubbing the edges *lengthwise* along a long *flat* file. Even new plastic pieces of equipment should be checked for accuracy.

The perpendicularity of the two scales of a drafting machine should be checked *every few months* for correctness.

Errors in direction of projection lines may be caused by an inaccurate triangle, T-square or drawing board.

FIG. 330. Error due to incorrect projection line.

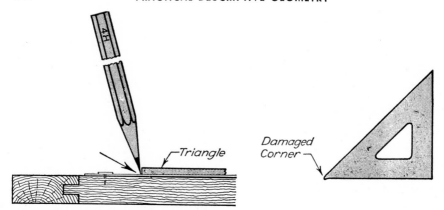

The accuracy in making a drawing may be improved considerably in the layout stage by using a sharp, reasonably hard pencil and keeping the point in the "corner" when drawing lines. Triangles, T-square and board should be checked regularly.

Damaged corners of triangles should be corrected otherwise an appreciable amount of inaccuracy will occur.

(a)   (b)

FIG. 331. Reducing inaccuracy.

241. INTERSECTING-LINE ERRORS

If a line is to be considered accurate if it is within $\frac{1}{64}$ in. of its correct position, the limits to either side of the correct position will be $\frac{1}{32}$ in. apart. Thus if two lines intersect at 90°, the intersection may be considered to be *any place* within a $\frac{1}{32}$ in. square, as the black square of Fig. 332, which is double in size, indicates.

If, however, the lines do not intersect at 90° but do intersect at 75°, the

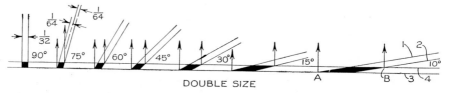

DOUBLE SIZE

If the intersecting projection lines had fallen along lines 1 and 3, the projection point to the top view would have been point A. However, if the projection lines had coincided with lines 2 and 4, the projection point to the top view would have been point B. These are the extremes for a tolerance of $\pm\frac{1}{64}$" in accuracy of location of each of the two lines. The magnification of this tolerance due to the small angle between the projection lines is approximately eleven times the $\frac{1}{32}$" allowable range for each line.

FIG. 332. Intersections-of-lines inaccuracies.

limits of projection to the next view have been magnified without going beyond the $\frac{1}{32}$-in. limits. Assume that the horizontal line actually drawn happened to be on the lower limit and the one at 45° to be along the upper limit. Then the point of intersection to be projected to the top view would be the extreme left corner of the black parallelogram. Now change to the other pair of limits of the 45° intersection, and the point to be projected to the top view would be the extreme right corner of the parallelogram. The top view of this intersection has a very good chance of being considerably in error. Observe the inaccuracy that two lines intersecting at 10° can produce.

In Fig. 333 point N_T is being projected to the front view of line AB. The area about N_T has been enlarged. Note that a pair of lines intersecting at 18° can magnify the normal $\frac{1}{32}$ range of limitation of accuracy for an elevation location of point N as much as 6.31 times. Revolution or an auxiliary view would reduce this magnification considerably.

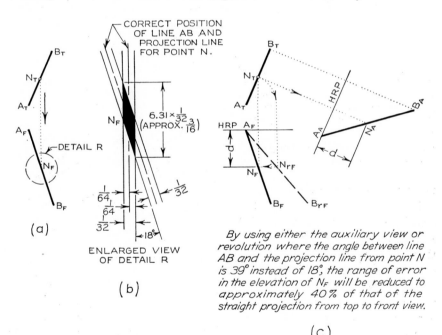

By using either the auxiliary view or revolution where the angle between line AB and the projection line from point N is 39° instead of 18°, the range of error in the elevation of N_F will be reduced to approximately 40% of that of the straight projection from top to front view.

(c)

Fig. 333. Intersection-of-lines inaccuracy.

Figure 334 shows the inaccuracy which can be produced in the given view as well as in the next view projected from it when a point is projected to the "side" of a circle or arc. It is altogether possible that a measurement from another view could have located the point on the circle, thereby avoiding this projection entirely.

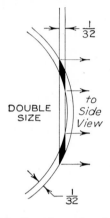

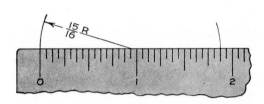

Inaccuracies in size of arcs and circles may be reduced by drawing two arcs opposite each other and measuring the diameter.

Fig. 335. Reducing inaccuracy of radii.

The projection of a point from the top to the front view (or vice versa) onto a circle or arc is likely to produce an appreciable error as the projection line approaches tangency with the circle or arc.

Fig. 334. Projection-line and circle-intersection inaccuracy.

242. SIZES OF ARCS AND CIRCLES

If an arc or circle is to be drawn, set the compass as closely as possible to the correct radius; then draw two arcs opposite to each other as shown in Fig. 335 and check with the scale to see if the diameter is correct. An error in radius is *doubled* in error on the diameter.

Figure 336 shows a surface to be either projected to another view or projected to that view from another view. Instead of locating both ends of lines I and

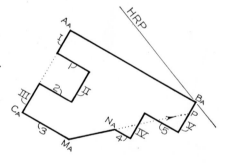

The tolerance of $\pm\frac{1}{64}''$ in locating points for the ends of short parallel lines can produce discrepancies in the parallelism of the lines as they are projected from view to view. Where possible check parallelism of the short lines with a longer line or extend one of them to where it will cross another line of the plane, then project the longer line. All views of the lines II, IV and V should be drawn parallel to AC. Draw lines I and III in line from A to C. Line MN may be better projected to another view by extending it to point P.

Fig. 336. Projections-of-short-lines inaccuracies.

III, locate C_A and A_A and see that the closer ends of each line are on the longer line $C_A A_A$.

Line $A_A B_A$ is a *relatively long* line, and it has other lines parallel to it. Line $A_A B_A$ will be much more nearly correct in direction than any of the shorter lines parallel to it; therefore the shorter lines should be drawn parallel to the longer and more nearly correctly located line.

The short sloping line MN may be more accurately located by extending it and projecting MP.

243. DIRECTIONS OF LINES THROUGH POINTS

The range of limits of accuracy in locating a line is $\frac{1}{32}$ in. as previously explained. The range of limit of accuracy in locating a point is a circle of $\frac{1}{64}$ radius or $\frac{1}{32}$ diameter. Two such circles of *actual* size are shown in Fig. 337. The line actually obtained by drawing a line through points A and B could be anywhere between the limits 1 and 2. The far end of the line increases in possibility of linear error the farther it is from point B. Thus a long line drawn through two points close together *must be assumed* to be appreciably in error.

Point "C" of line ABC will lie somewhere between the limits 1 and 2 depending on its distance from B.

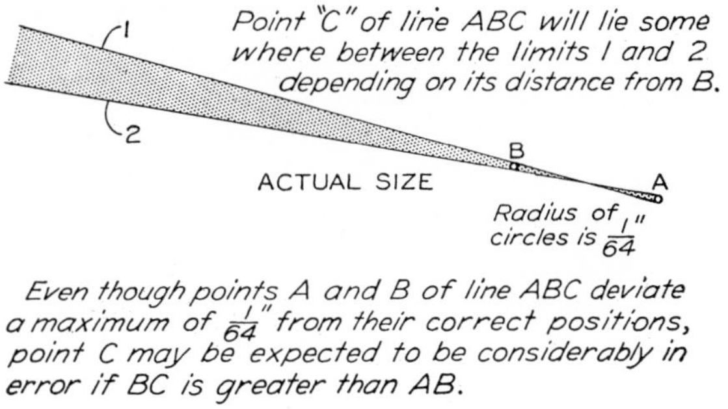

Fig. 337. (*Right*) Inaccuracy of long lines through two points close together.

ACTUAL SIZE

Radius of circles is $\frac{1}{64}$"

Even though points A and B of line ABC deviate a maximum of $\frac{1}{64}$" from their correct positions, point C may be expected to be considerably in error if BC is greater than AB.

$\frac{1}{64}$" radius

ACTUAL SIZE

A (Given)

$\frac{1}{32}$

E (Given)

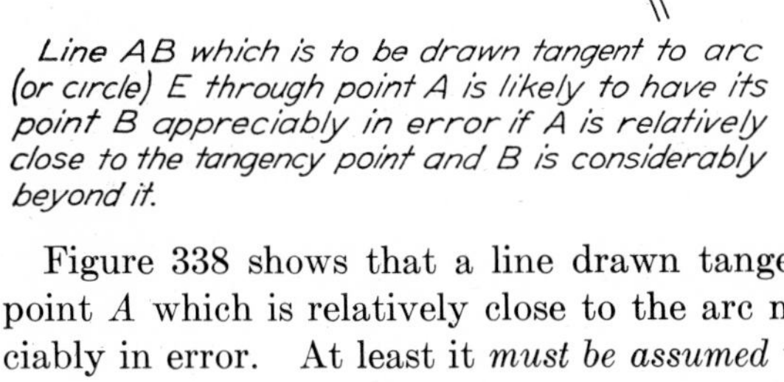

Fig. 338. (*Left*) Inaccuracy of long lines tangent to a circle and through a point close to the circle.

Line AB which is to be drawn tangent to arc (or circle) E through point A is likely to have its point B appreciably in error if A is relatively close to the tangency point and B is considerably beyond it.

Figure 338 shows that a line drawn tangent to the arc and through point A which is relatively close to the arc may have its far end appreciably in error. At least it *must be assumed* to be appreciably in error.

Figure 339 shows that a long line cannot be drawn parallel to a short one with any degree of assurance that it will actually be parallel to the short line.   The short line itself may be appreciably in error.   See limit lines *between* A and B in Fig. 337.

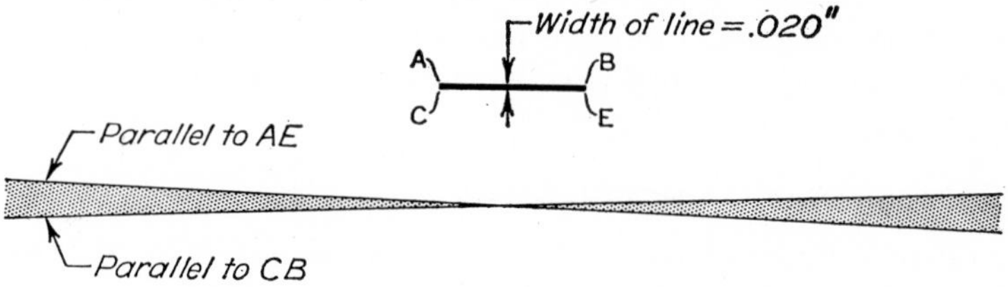

A long line drawn parallel to the above short line will lie somewhere within the shaded area and may be expected to be inaccurately drawn. Where possible avoid drawing a long line parallel to a short one.

FIG. 339. Inaccuracy of long lines parallel to short lines.

244. AVOIDING THE INACCURACIES

The applications of the above items of possible inaccuracies are so varied that it is hardly feasible to attempt to generalize on methods to avoid them.   Instead, each case must be considered on its own merits and solved individually.

The purpose of this chapter, which is the first of its kind in any book, is to call attention to the possibilities and the magnitudes of the inaccuracies. *Awareness* as to where the inaccuracies occur and a *desire* to avoid them invariably find a satisfactory method for avoiding or reducing them to a respectable minimum.

HOW TO USE AN INDEX

Let us assume it is desired to find the references for the intersection of a cylinder with a cone. This title may be looked up under the following headings:

Cone, intersection with cylinder,
Cylinder, intersection with cone,
Intersection of cone with cylinder,
Intersection of cylinder with cone,
Line of intersection, cone with cylinder,
Line of intersection, cylinder with cone.

It is not to be assumed that this title may be found under all of these headings. The index is cross referenced, but space does not permit such an elaborate cross index for each and every title. If the title cannot be found under one heading, consider other possible cross references and look for the title under another heading.

References are to pages; 125–128 means pages 125 to 128 inclusive.

A

Accuracy, graphical, 243
Addition, of lines to plane, 43, 44, 102
  of points, to line, 32, 33, 47
  to plane, 45
Angle, of line with any plane, 70, 71, 88, 90, 91
  with *FRP*, 68, 89
  with *HRP*, 67, 88
  with *PRP*, 69, 89
  between planes, 80–82, 107
  bisector of, 50
Auxiliary views, 17
  basic reasons for, 30
  points common to, 24
  primary, 25
  projected, off front view, 20

Auxiliary views, projected, off side view, 22
  off top view, 17
  secondary, 25
  series of, 27
Auxiliary reference plane (*ARP*), 17

B

Bearing of a line, 135
Bisector of an angle, 50

C

Cirele, great, 182
  line tangent to, 117
  size of, 246
Circular elements, 113
Civil engineering, 135, 136, 141–143
  cuts and fills, 141, 143

Common perpendicular to skew lines, 41, 62, 63
  views, 24
Concentric circle ellipse construction, 126
Cone, definition of, 114
  development of, 186, 187
  elements of, 114, 115
  intersection of, with cylinder, 216–218, 220, 224, 236
    with plane, 178
    with second cone, 226, 227
    with surface of revolution, 235
    with torus, 236
  locating a point on, 116
  oblique and right circular, 114
  piercing points of a line with, 122
  plane tangent to, 116
  of revolution, 87, 88, 90
  shadow of, 148
  tangent to cylinder, 218
  transitions, 198
  visibility of elements of, 115, 116
  warped, 171
Conic sections, 125
Conical transitions, 198
Conoid, 169
Contour elements, 113, 233
Contour lines, 135, 136, 141
Convolute, 154
Counterrevolution, 102
Cow's horn, 172
Curved surfaces, 154
Cut and fill, 136, 141–143
Cutting planes, 206
  sphere method, 233
Cylinder, definition of, 113
  development of, 183, 203
  elements of, 113
    visibility of, 116
  intersection of, with cone, 216–218, 236
    with cylinder, 207–214, 236
    with plane, 176, 240
    with sphere, 230
    with torus, 228, 235, 241
    types of, 211
  locating a point on, 116
  oblique and right circular, 114
  piercing points of a line with, 121
  plane tangent to, 116
  shadow of, 149
  tangent to a cone, 218
Cylindroid, 170

D

Development, of a cone, 186, 187
  of a cylinder, 183, 203

Developments, definition of, 183
  of a prism, 190
  of a pyramid, 191
  of a sphere, 189
  of a warped surface, 192
  of a warped-surface transition, 196
Diagram, true-length, 188, 194–196
  vector or force, 108
Dip, 136, 137
Double-curved line, 185, 200
Double-curved surfaces, 154, 172
Drill hole, 136

E

Edge view of a plane, 47
Elements, circular, 113
  of a cone, 116
  contour, 113
  of a cylinder, 113
  straight-line, 113
  visibility of, 115
Ellipse, 125–128, 132
Ellipsoid, oblate, 173, 174
  prolate, 173, 174
Engineering drawing, 7
Equipment errors, 243
Extreme positions of revolution, 85

F

Fault, 136
Fill and cuts, 136, 141–143
Force diagrams, 108
Frontal lines, 14
  addition of, to a plane, 44
Frontal reference plane (FRP), 3
  angle with, of line, 68, 89
  of plane, 78

G

Geological terminology, 136
Grade, 69, 70
Graphical accuracy, 243
Great circle, 182

H

Hanging wall, 136
Helicoid, oblique, 160, 164
  right, 160, 162, 163, 197
Helix angle, on a cone, 202
  on a cylinder, 200
  definition of, 200
  right-hand and left-hand, 202
  on a surface of revolution, 202

Horizontal lines, 14
  addition of, to planes, 44
  shortest, between skew lines, 65
Horizontal reference plane (*HRP*), 3
  angle with, of line, 67, 88
    of plane, 78
Hyperbola, 125, 133
Hyperbolic paraboloid, 167
Hyperboloid of revolution, 87, 158, 173,
  174

I

Inaccuracies, 243
  avoidance of, 248
Inclined lines, 12
Inclined plane, 13
  angle of line with, 70, 71, 88, 90
Intersecting lines, 33, 244
Intersection, change of visibility of, 206,
  207
  choice of cutting planes for, 205, 206
  of cone (*see* Cone)
  by cutting-sphere method, 237, 240
  of cylinder (*see* Cylinder)
  great circle, 182
  line of, 74, 75, 77
  by parallel-cylinder method, 237, 240
  of plane (*see* Plane)
  of planes, 74, 75, 77
  practical problem of, 175
  of surfaces, 205
  tangent to contour elements, 233
  types of, 222
  of veins, 140

L

Lateral edges, 190
Line of intersection of planes, 74, 75, 77
Lines, 12, 247
  addition of, to plane, 43, 44, 102
  addition of points to, 32, 33, 47
  angle of (*see* Angle of lines)
  bearing of, 135
  contour, 135
  frontal, 14
  horizontal, 14
  inclined, 12
  intersecting, 33, 244
  nonintersecting, 33
  nonparallel, 35
  normal, 12
  oblique, 13
  parallel, 35, 248
    to plane, 52

Lines, perpendicular, 38
  to planes, 56
  piercing points of, 58, 59
  planes parallel to, 53, 54
  planes perpendicular to, 58
  point view of, 41
  points on, 31, 247
  points revolved about, 85
  profile, 15
  replacing, 45
  revolving lines about, 87, 98
  slope of, 42, 69, 70
  tangent to circle, 117
  theoretical, 15
  true length of, 37, 88–91
  visibility of, 50

M

Mining, 135
  terminology, 136

N

Nonintersecting lines, 33
Nonparallel lines, 35
Normal lines, 12
Normal planes, 13

O

Oblique circular cylinder, 114
Oblique cone transitions, 198
Oblique lines, 13
Oblique planes, 14
  angles of lines with, 70, 71, 88, 90
  revolution of, 100–103
Outcrop, 136 ,137

P

Parabola, 125, 130
Parabolic cylinder, 113
Paraboloid, 173, 174
  hyperbolic, 167
  plane tangent to a, 120
Parallel-cylinder intersection method,
  237, 240
Parallel lines, 35
  to plane, 52
Parallel planes, 53, 55
Perpendicular lines, 38
  common to skew lines, 41, 62, 63
Perpendicular planes, 58
Piercing of points of lines, with cone, 122
  with cylinder, 121
  with plane, 58, 59

Plane, addition to, of frontal and horizontal lines, 44
  of lines, 43, 102
  of points, 45
  of profile lines, 44
  angle between, and *FRP*, 78, 118
    and *HRP*, 78, 118
    and other planes, 80–82, 107
    and *PRP*, 79, 118
  angle of line with, 70, 71, 88, 90, 91
  auxiliary reference, 17
  definition of, 46–47
  edge view of, 47
  frontal reference, 3
  horizontal reference, 3
  inclined, 13
  intersection of, with cone, 178
    with cylinder, 176, 240
    with plane, 74, 75, 77
    with sphere, 181
    with torus, 179
  line parallel to, 52
  line perpendicular to, 56
  normal, 13
  oblique (*see* Oblique planes)
  parallel to, line, 53
    plane, 53–55
  perpendicular to line and plane, 58
  reference (*see* Reference planes)
  representation of, 16
  revolution of, 100–106
  revolved about line, 103
  slope of, 69
  tangent to, cone, 116, 118
    cylinder, 116, 118
    paraboloid, 120
    sphere, 58, 120
  theoretical, 15
  true size of, 48, 100, 101
  views of, 9
  visibility of, 50
Point, addition of, to line, 31, 32, 47
  to plane, 45
  on cone, 116
  on cylinder, 116
  on line, 31, 32, 47
  revolution of, 85
  on sphere, 124
Point view of line, 41
Practical intersection problems, 175
Primary auxiliary view, 25
Prism, development of, 190
Profile lines, 15
Profile reference plane (*PRP*), 6, 7
  angle with, of line, 69, 89
  of plane, 79

Profile reference plane (*see also* Reference planes)
Projecting a line onto a plane, 61
Pyramid, development of, 191

R

Railroad cut, 136
Reference planes, 3
  angle of line with, 67–69, 88–92
  auxiliary, 17
  direction of edge view of, 25
  foreshortening of, 18
  frontal, 3
  generalization of, 7
  horizontal, 3
  oblique, 25
  profile (*see* Profile reference plane)
  regular, 3
Replacing of lines, 45
Representing a plane, 16
  at specified angle, 95, 118
Resultant, 108, 109
Revolution, angle by, between line and plane, 87–91
  between lines and reference planes, 87–90
  between planes, 107
  basic elements of, 84
  cone of, 87–91
  extreme positions of, 85
  of line, about line, 87, 98
    for true length, 88–91
  path of, 84, 85
  of plane, into *HRP*, 100, 103
    about line, 103
    for true size, 100, 101
  purpose of, 84
  surfaces of, 154, 155
Right circular cylinders, 114
Right sections, 81, 107, 183, 190
Ruled surfaces, 154

S

Secondary auxiliary views, 25
Series of auxiliary views, 27
Shades and shadows, 144
Shadows, cast on cylinders, 148
  cast on planes, 145–148
  of cones, 148
  of cylinders, 149
  of lines, 145–148
  of objects, 151
  ray of light for, 150
  of spheres, 150, 152
Skew lines, common perpendicular to, 41, 62, 63

Skew lines, with connecting line at speci-
    fied slope, 96
  shortest horizontal connection, 65
  shortest line at specified slope, 66
Slope, of line, 69
  of plane, 69, 70
Space directions, 32
Sphere, 174
  conoid tangent to, 170
  development of, 189
  intersection of, with cylinder, 230
    with plane, 181
  plane tangent to, 58, 120
  points on, 124
  shadow of a, 150, 152
Sphere method, 218
  cutting-, 233
Strike line, 136, 137
Surfaces of revolution, 154, 172
  intersection of, with cone, 235
    with cylinder, 235

            T

Tangent cone and cylinder, 218
Tangent plane, with cone, 116, 118
  with cylinder, 116, 118
  with paraboloid, 120
  with sphere, 58, 120
Tangent sphere with conoid, 170
Torus, 173, 174
  intersection of, with cone, 236
    with cylinder, 228, 235, 241

Torus, intersection of, with plane, 179
Trammel method, 126
Transitions, 193, 196, 198
Triangles and T square, use of, 29
True-length diagram, 188, 192–196
  of double curved line, 185, 200
  of lines, 37
True size of a plane, 48, 100, 101
Tunnel, 136

            U

Use of triangles, 29

            V

Vector diagrams, 108
Veins, 136–140
  intersection of, 140
Views of a plane, 9
  common, 24
  construction of, 10
Visibility, of elements, 115
  of intersections, 206, 207
  of lines, 50
  of planes, 50

            W

Warped cone, 171
Warped-surface development, 192
Warped-surface transitions, 196
Warped surfaces, 154, 157